LIVES IN THE BALANCE

Lives in the Balance

Dr Debbie Lovell

eagle
Guildford, Surrey

Copyright © 2000 Dr Debbie Lovell

The right of Debbie Lovell to be identified as author of this work has been asserted by her in accordance with the Copyright, Design and Patents Act 1988.

British Library Cataloguing in Publication Data. A catalogue record for this book is available from the British Library.

Published by Eagle Publishing Ltd,
PO Box 530, Guildford, Surrey GU2 4FH.

Scripture quotations are taken from the Holy Bible, New International Version. Copyright © 1973, 1978, 1984 by International Bible Society. Used by permission of Hodder & Stoughton, a Division of Hodder Headline.

Typeset by Eagle
Printed by Cox & Wyman
ISBN No: 0 86347 392 X

Contents

In loving memory of my mother Jean,
who died shortly before this book was published.

Introduction

1

My Own Story of Hope

As I write this, there are two young women in the room with me. One of them looks as though she might die at any moment. She says that is what she wants. She shivers with cold underneath her baggy jumper. The jumper hides her stick-like arms, but her frailty is still obvious. Although she is seventeen, she looks more like an eleven-year-old, as her body has no curves. Her gaunt face appears almost grey, and there is no sparkle in her eyes. Her hair has been falling out in handfuls. Her body is so cold that it has produced a layer of thin, downy hair over her face, in an effort to keep warm. She finds it painful to sit in one position for long, as she has no padding over her bones.

Just as a hungry animal will not sit still as it looks desperately for food, so she has a restlessness about her, but she continually moves away from food, rather than towards it. She will not even lick a stamp, because she worries that the gum might contain calories. Not only does she fear weight gain, but she also believes that she does not deserve anything good. The little she does eat tends to be food which has gone off, bruised fruit, food intended for animals, or leftovers which have been thrown into the litter bin. She believes that is all she deserves: the rejected scraps. In her mind she, too, is a rejected scrap of life. She hates herself, and punishes herself by slapping her face hard or digging her nails into her skin, although she never does this when anyone else is around. Far from seeking attention, she longs to be left alone to die.

She seems without hope in all respects. Physically, her body is packing up. A scan shows that her bones are like those of a seventy-year-old woman – they are so brittle that they look as if they could be broken by a mere hug. Perhaps it is just as well that she never receives a hug. Sometimes she collapses in the street while trying to make herself run. She feels faint when she stands up, as her blood pressure is very low. She wets herself both during the day and at night, as she has lost control over the muscles that regulate her bladder. She tends to wake early, and sometimes is unable to move a muscle for a few minutes after waking, which frightens her.

The problems are not only physical. Emotionally, she is frozen. She barely knows what emotions are, as she has convinced herself that it is wrong to feel sad or angry, and she has forgotten what joy is. Just surviving takes up all her energy, and there is none left for an emotional life. She has no intimate relationships. She does not let anyone know what she is really like inside, because she feels ashamed of herself and fears rejection. She could not imagine having a boyfriend. She has very little self-confidence, and never offers her own opinion, as she believes she has nothing worthwhile to say. When she does speak, her voice is a low, monotonous depressed drone.

Intellectually, too, there are some difficulties. She has struggled since starting school. While other children were learning to spell 'encyclopaedia', she was in a remedial group, trying to master the spelling of 'road'. The less verbal subjects seem no easier. She has difficulty in making sense of maps or diagrams, or even telling left from right. This causes problems in subjects such as geography, art and technical drawing. Until recently she has, by sheer determination, managed to overcome these difficulties and do well. She is driven by a desire to please her parents and her teachers, and she will study for fourteen hours a day, timing herself obsessively. But self-starvation has made it hard to concentrate or to think in abstract terms, and her memory is failing. Her starving brain keeps reminding her about food. She resists the temptation to eat, and forces herself to continue working, telling herself that if she finishes this essay, she can have a two-minute toilet break in sixty minutes time.

Socially, she has no desire to be with other people. She believes that she is boring and would spoil any social gathering, and so she tries to avoid social events, especially those which involve food. When she does go to a party to please her parents, she takes a book with her, hoping that she will be able to sit in a corner and study. There is little spare capacity in her mind to think about other people, and she does not realise how worried her family are, as they watch her fade away. She has distanced herself from everyone.

What about her spiritual life? She is a committed Christian, and is looking forward to death, as she longs to be with Jesus. Sadly, even her spiritual life seems bleak. Far from providing joy and freedom, it has become a series of rituals fed by guilt. She lives in a world of deceit and self-abuse. She appears hopeless – physically, emotionally, intellectually, socially and spiritually.

The second woman in the room is watching her carefully. This woman is quite a different character. People describe her as 'a picture of health'. She has just returned from a holiday, and looks peaceful and relaxed. Her weight is within the healthy range for her height. She enjoys sharing meals with friends, and is not obsessed with food. Eating is a natural part of her day, which she gives little thought to.

Unlike her skinny sister, she is very aware of feelings – both her own, and other people's. In fact, her job is in the realm of emotions, as she works as a clinical psychologist. She is confident and can be assertive when she needs to be. Her intellectual ability is not in question; she holds not one but two doctorates. Despite this, she does not devote her whole life to academia. She enjoys her work, but sees people as more important than work, and she loves socialising. She is known for

11

organising parties and playing silly games. She has a lively sense of humour and wants to live life to the full. One of her pleasures is travelling, and she goes overseas for a few weeks every year, combining work with pleasure. She has many friends, and among these are a small group of people with whom she shares the things that are closest to her heart. They, in turn, share their true selves with her. She and her boyfriend pray together, seek to be honest with each other, and enjoy a depth of intimacy which the first woman does not know is possible. Their intimacy does not extend to sexual experiences, as both the woman and her boyfriend are committed Christians, but this woman, unlike the first, is able to accept her own sexuality, and does not feel repulsed by it.

While the first woman follows rituals in an attempt to please the God whom she fears, the second woman chats freely to God her Father throughout her day, and enjoys being in his presence and listening to him. She knows deep inside that he loves her. She has experienced remarkable answers to prayer, and is full of love for both God and other people, unlike the first woman who has never really learned what love is. The second woman knows that she is far from perfect, but she does not despise herself. She accepts herself, with all her strengths and weaknesses, and she trusts that God will continue to help her become the person he wants her to be. She looks forward to the future with hope.

So, here I am with these two very different women. One appears trapped, stunted, and hopeless. The second seems free, flourishing, and full of hope. The first is the person I was twelve years ago, when I was suffering from anorexia nervosa. The second is how I see myself today, moulded by my past experiences, but also freed from them. I will try to share something of my journey.

Some of my earliest memories relate to being bullied at school. I was teased because I wore glasses, and because my clothes were unfashionable, coming from jumble sales or being passed down from my older sister. In order to try and buy friendship, I stole money from my mother's handbag, and bought football stickers which I gave away. When I was caught I felt extremely ashamed. I tried to make up by becoming exceptionally good and working very hard at school, in an attempt to please my teachers and my parents. This led to further bullying, as I was seen as a 'teacher's pet'. Most of the bullying was verbal, but there were also occasions when I was spat at, or physically hurt, or my possessions were damaged or thrown away, or people tried to tear my clothes from me. I never retaliated. Instead I concluded that I must deserve this treatment. My family did not tend to show affection or emotions – for instance, we did not hug each other, and I was taught that kisses were unhygienic. I grew up feeling unloved and unlovable.

There were good things in life too, and these helped me to cope with the bad times. Sometimes my parents took us on an outing at the weekend, perhaps to climb a mountain, which I enjoyed. I always looked forward to the summer holidays, as every year we spent these with my grandparents, who made me feel special. Spending time with friends also helped me forget my problems. Most of my small group of friends were also bullied. It helped to know that I wasn't the only one who was laughed at, and we supported each other.

I tried to be friendly to the people who bullied me, because I wanted to follow the teachings of Jesus. My mother took me along to church week by week, and although I sometimes told her that I did not want to go, or I acted disruptively in her Sunday school class, in general I wanted to please God. When I was twelve years old I went to an evangelistic meeting. I realised there that I was not really a Christian, as I lived my life according to what I wanted, not what God wanted. I prayed for forgiveness, and asked Jesus to come and be at the centre of my life.

After this, I wanted other people to know God too, as I

realised that nothing could be more important. To make my classmates think about God, I started wearing stickers to school, asking questions such as, 'Where will you spend eternity?' It's hardly surprising that this led to more bullying!

Because my appearance and my behaviour were frequently mocked, I had little respect for myself. I believed that I was very ugly. I was determined not to make matters worse by becoming fat as well. My mother was often criticised for being over-weight, and I wanted to make sure that I didn't go the same way. At school we were warned about the dangers of 'fatty foods', which could cause heart attacks. Rather than reacting in a balanced way, I cut high-fat foods out of my diet completely. This gave me a sense of achievement – at least I could do something right. I also began to exercise, believing that this would help me keep fit and prevent weight gain. I did press-ups and sit-ups in my room, and I started jogging the mile and a half to school, carrying my heavy bag of books on my back.

When I was fourteen, the famine in Ethiopia started hitting the headlines. It was the first time that I had seen mass coverage of world hunger in the media, and I, like many other people, felt horrified by what I saw. The voice of self-hatred in my mind whispered to me, 'You ugly cow, how can you eat so much when all those people have nothing at all?' I started to feel guilty about eating, believing that I did not deserve good food. I took part in sponsored fasts to raise money for famine relief. During the period of Lent I gave up eating certain foods, and at least one day each week I went without lunch. The money saved by not eating was sent to those who needed the food more than I did. I started to feel quite pleased about my self-denial and fasting. After all, that was what Jesus wanted, wasn't it? At a time when I should have been going through a growth spurt, my weight started to slide off.

It was not very difficult for me to eat less. I had little sense of taste or smell, and so I wasn't tempted by flavours and scents as other people might be. When, as a game or as part of an experiment, I was blindfolded and asked to distinguish between different types of food or different flavours of crisps, I was clueless – it all tasted much the same to me. Perhaps this was because I was deficient in zinc or some other mineral linked to taste detection. Or perhaps I had blocked off my ability to taste following some early experiences of being forced to eat things which I did not want to (including burnt food, half-cooked meat with blood in it, and food with vomit on). Whatever the reason, I felt that being unable to taste was a bonus, as it helped reduce my desire to eat.

I also felt pleased rather than upset when my periods stopped as a result of my weight loss. I regarded menstruation as dirty and disgusting, and I was pleased to be rid of the inconvenience.

I did not think I was ill. Instead, I rationalised my self-starvation, telling myself that I was eating more than I needed. My thoughts became increasingly narrow, as my starving brain grew less able to cope with the complexities of life. I lost interest in things which I had previously enjoyed, including singing. My voice had become tinny, weak and comparatively tuneless. I withdrew from other people into a cocoon of self-loathing. I would not spend any money on myself, believing that I did not deserve it. When people gave me presents, I gave them away. I socialised as little as possible, as there seemed no point in it. I felt that all my time should be spent in useful pursuits, such as studying, or visiting the sick and elderly. I had been taught that I must never feel bored, and so I constantly kept myself busy. I was determined to achieve good marks at school. My parents and teachers wanted me to do well in every subject, and I didn't want to let them down. When I received 98 per cent in a mock O-level examination, my mother asked me, 'What happened to the other 2 per cent?' I took her comment not as a joke, but as a confirmation that only perfection was good enough.

We didn't speak about problems at home. I was aware that

my parents did not have a happy marital relationship, and I didn't want to worry them with my difficulties. They had enough worries of their own, and I simply wanted to please them. I found it difficult to please both of them, however, as they sometimes wanted different things, and at times I felt torn between them.

For a long time my weight loss went unnoticed. Eventually, however, people at church and at school began to comment. The word 'anorexia' started being mentioned. I knew very little about this illness, but I was sure that I didn't have it. For a start, I didn't make myself sick, and I thought that people with anorexia did. Secondly, I felt perfectly well, and I didn't think I was underweight at all. Thirdly, I believed I was eating a lot more than I needed, not less. Anyway, Christians didn't get that sort of problem, did they?

My mother eventually persuaded me to go with her to see our family doctor. I smiled at the doctor, showing her the happy mask which I liked to show the world. It worked. She concluded that I couldn't have anorexia, because I was too happy. She said I should try to gain some weight, and recommended that I eat a Mars Bar every day and go to more parties. Most seventeen-year-old girls would love such a prescription. I smiled compliantly and thought, 'No chance!' Parties seemed a waste of time in such a serious world, and I felt proud of not having eaten chocolate for years.

After this appointment I did try to eat a bit more. To please my mother I even ate a few squares of chocolate. However, by this time I was in the grip of anorexia, and my view had become distorted. What looked like a small amount of food to anyone else appeared a mountain to me. I believed I was greedy and shouldn't eat so much. I was afraid that my weight would soar if I started eating all the high calorie foods which my mother tried to tempt me with. Moreover, I felt depressed when I ate more. This may have been partly due to my feelings of guilt, disgust and fear around eating, and partly because the starving brain releases endorphins (natural opiates) which gave me a sense of being 'high'. Eating more caused me to lose this sense of well-being, and I was also physically uncomfortable because my stomach had shrunk.

Research in the 1950s showed that even healthy young men became obsessed with thoughts of food, and adopted strange rituals, when they followed a semi-starvation diet over a period of six months. Starvation alters our thought processes and can become like an addiction. I was certainly under the influence of anorexia. Like an alcoholic, I resorted to deceit to feed (or starve) my habit. I told my mother white lies about what I had eaten. I rationalised this by telling myself that self-denial and fasting were biblical practices which I should follow, whatever anyone else said.

I convinced myself that I was behaving as a Christian should. In retrospect, I can see that I was, in a sense, breaking every one of the ten commandments. I coveted, wishing that I was someone else, a better and prettier person. I lied, pretending that I had eaten when I had not. I stole food from dustbins and took outdated food from fridges, believing that I should not spend money on myself, but could eat anything that would otherwise be thrown away. I did not commit adultery in a literal sense (and in fact, I felt disgusted at the thought of sex); but I was having an affair with an eating disorder – my secret, shameful life, which consumed my thoughts. I did not murder anyone else, but I was slowly killing myself. I deceived my parents, and would not honour them by doing the one thing they wanted, which was to fight this obsession. I would not rest on the Sabbath, as I was afraid of rest; if I allowed myself to think, I might become aware of my inner pain. So on Sundays I stopped studying only to busy myself with writing letters of encouragement to missionaries, visiting elderly people, and helping out at home.

I justified my self-torture by saying that I was fasting to please God. In so doing, I was using God's name in vain. I idolised both work and self-control. Anorexia had become my god.

My weight continued to fall. My mother took me to see several different GPs, in an attempt to find out what the problem was. Eventually a consultant diagnosed me as having anorexia nervosa. I was admitted to hospital, weighing about five stone, which was a critically low weight for my height.

This came as a severe shock. I told myself that the diagnosis must be a mistake. I hated being in hospital. For six weeks I was not allowed to leave my bed. I even had to use a commode, as I was not allowed to walk to the toilet. I was given three large meals every day as well as snacks and special high calorie drinks. I found it very uncomfortable, both physically and emotionally, to go so quickly from eating very little to consuming such a lot of food. I was generally compliant as I wanted to please people, but when I could get away with eating less, I did.

While I was in hospital, I felt overwhelmed by all the cards and visitors I received. I had thought that I was worthless and unlovable and that no one really liked me, but day after day people demonstrated how much they cared about me. Friends from school and church kept coming to visit me, and I realised that they were genuinely concerned. My family were wonderful. My parents visited me almost every day, often with my younger brother as well, and my sister travelled all the way from Birmingham to Aberdeen to visit for a few days. I felt overwhelmed by these displays of love. I became determined to get better for the sake of my friends and family, and so that I could help other people and share God's love with them.

During the weeks of bed-rest I had plenty of time to cry out to God. Until then I had always tried to *do* things to please God – helping with the Sunday school; washing up at the lunch-club for senior citizens; collecting money for charity; singing in the church choir; and so on. I had very rarely watched television or relaxed, even on Christmas Day, because I felt that I should always be either working or doing something for other people. Anything else would be selfish. Now that I was confined to bed there was little that I could do, other than pray. It took me a long time to realise that what pleased God most was my relationship with him, not any tasks which I did.

There was a similarity between my relationship with God, and my relationship with my father. I had always tried to please my father – for example, by taking him a cup of tea in bed every morning; gaining good marks at school; learning to play the violin (which I disliked), and generally keeping quiet at home and staying out of his way. I felt afraid of him. While I was in hospital, I began to get to know my dad as a person. During his visits we did crosswords together, or chatted about trivia. I liked this, and I got the feeling that he liked it too. In a similar way, my relationship with God had been based on a sense of fear and duty, without true love. Stripped of all my 'good deeds', I came before God with nothing to offer except myself. I slowly began to learn that God loved me not because of anything that I did, but because he was my Father. Over time I came to realise that my worth did not depend on what I did, but on what God had done for me. My worth certainly did not depend on what I weighed or what I ate. I read in the Bible that God loved me. Although I didn't feel lovable, I knew that God was not a liar, and I chose to try to believe him.

The realisation that I was of value began while I was in hospital, but was still not complete by the time I was finally allowed to go home. I spent eight weeks in hospital before I reached my target weight of seven stone. When I was discharged, I initially felt so relieved to be free from being forced to eat, that I started to control my eating again and lost some weight. Nevertheless, I was determined that I would not slide back too far, and I managed to maintain most of the weight which I had gained. I went back to school to complete my final year. I also became involved with a few social activities and other interests – something which I would not have done before.

My hospital treatment had been focused almost entirely on my gaining weight, with little attention paid to my psychological state. After I was discharged, my parents, my brother and I participated in two sessions of family therapy. Years later, I read a copy of my medial notes. The psychologist's report to my GP stated, 'It was obvious that Deborah was caught in the middle of her parents, unable to act as siding with one meant hurting the othe . . .' That seemed to be an accurate observation, and the therapy helped us as a family to begin to change. I also had a few sessions of individual therapy with a social worker. These helped me to make decisions about my future, and increased my self-confidence.

I was keen to use my experiences to help other people. An early opportunity came when, six months after I left hospital, my mother showed me a letter in a local newspaper from a girl with anorexia. I wrote to the girl, via the paper. I wanted to offer her hope, from my own experience, as I felt that I had overcome the worst of the problem. My letter was opened at the newspaper office, and a journalist contacted me to ask if I would allow them to write an article about my recovery. Initially I winced at the thought of this, as I felt ashamed of the fact that I had suffered from a mental illness, and especially an eating disorder, as such problems are often misunderstood and regarded as attention-seeking behaviour. However, I decided that the risk of being criticised was worth taking if I could help other people, and perhaps help increase understanding. I agreed to be interviewed, and the article was duly published. I did receive comments about it, but none of them were negative, and I began to feel accepted despite my past.

Nevertheless, after another six months I was glad to move 400 miles away to study psychology and English at Keele University. I wanted a fresh start in a place where people might know me as someone other than 'the one who was anorexic'. As part of my fresh identity, I started introducing myself as 'Debbie' rather than 'Deborah'. This felt very strange to me, as my parents disliked the name 'Debbie' and I had always gone along with their wishes in the past, but as I was now so far from home, I decided that it would not harm them if I shortened my name, and so I did.

At university, I enjoyed the work, my social life and the feeling of independence. A special blessing was that during my first year the cost of my weekday meals was included in the accommodation fee. This meant that I did not feel guilty about spending money on food and I was able to eat well. I tended to save some bread and fruit from the weekday meals to eat at the weekends so that I did not have to buy food, as I still felt that I should give money away rather than spend it on myself. Not many students would be able to save as much money as I did! I was obviously eating enough, as I found when I returned home for Christmas that I had put on weight. I convinced myself that this was a positive thing as I knew that I was still at the low end of a healthy weight. I was determined to get well.

As I grew stronger physically, I also grew spiritually. I gave up some of my rituals (such as timing myself when I prayed to ensure that I spent enough time in prayer), and I felt much freer. My relationship with God became more joyful, and less bound by duty. I was asked to help lead student Bible studies, and we chose to consider some controversial topics, such as abortion and euthanasia. Previously I would have shied away from offering any opinions, instead accepting what others said and judging my own views as less valid. Now I realised that it was good to work out my own views. I encouraged others in the group also to think things through for themselves. In my work, too, I began to give my own opinions about the texts which we were studying or the theories under discussion. I became more assertive as I tried to defend my views.

In my position as a Christian Union representative for my hall of residence, I found that some people came to talk with me about difficulties they were facing. I had never come across such honest sharing of feelings before, and I was pleased that people were willing to trust me in this way. I started being more open in return, so that the friendships deepened and became two-way. Previously, I had felt the need to wear a smiling mask which said, 'I'm OK' and hide any concerns or hurts. I worried that if people knew 'the real me' they would reject me. I also thought that to be a good Christian witness, I was meant to have no needs and no problems. My new friendships helped me take this mask off and be myself. They also helped me become aware of, and face up to, my own feelings. I discovered that Jesus himself was quite willing to admit his needs, for instance by asking for a drink of water or for his friends to accompany him. He was even willing to cry. As I learned to allow my needs and emotions to surface, instead of repressing them, I felt that my life was becoming much more colourful.

During the summer holiday after my second year at university, I went to Swaziland to work in a boarding school as a short-term missionary. This helped boost my confidence even further. The summer had its moments – such as the evening the pupils decided to riot and I locked myself in the storeroom while they banged on the door! Despite this, I loved the Swazi people. I had often thought that I would like to live in a country where people were not judged by their appearance, or at least not as much as they were in Britain. In Britain I felt ugly, but in Swaziland I felt accepted, and my looks didn't seem to matter. The relaxed lifestyle helped me to be more relaxed too, and to begin to consider people more of a priority than tasks.

When I returned to England work took precedence again, as I still had a streak of perfectionism, and I wanted to achieve the best degree I could manage. The hard work paid off, and to my delight I gained a first class honours degree. I then worked for three months in an adolescent unit. Many of the young people were in the unit because of their aggressive behaviour, which their families could no longer cope with. Violent incidents were common in the unit, and I didn't get away unharmed. Hearing about the difficult backgrounds of many of the adolescents, I felt that it was not surprising that they had turned to violence, and I was keen to do what I could to help them.

While I had been suffering from anorexia, I had recorded my thoughts and experiences in a diary. Various people had suggested that I should try to publish this account, in order to help others. I used some of my spare time that summer to type up my story, mainly for my own benefit, as it was therapeutic to look back and see how I had changed. After typing my account, I asked my parents if they would like to read it. I found it both frightening and healing to let them read the secrets which I had never shared with them, including the ways in which I had deceived them. I tentatively raised the possibility of trying to publish my story. If they had been opposed to that, I would have given up the idea, as I did not want to cause them any further pain or embarrassment. They both encouraged me to try to find a publisher. I felt that demonstrated how we had changed as a family. There was a new willingness to admit our mistakes, and to be open about our emotions. The book, which I had called *Hungry for Love*, was published in 1994. The first copy was given to Princess Diana, as we had corresponded following her speech at the International Conference on Eating Disorders in 1993.

I was delighted when I received letters from people who had found the book helpful. I was especially touched by a letter from my grandmother, who had always been a very private person. After reading the book, she wrote, 'Anorexia nervosa was unknown to us, and "why you" who was such a loved and loving child is so hard to accept. I can only think that he [God] chose you, so that having overcome such dreadful emotions you are now able to help other people with similar problems'. I was thrilled to think that God could use even the experience of my illness for good.

While I was working in the adolescent unit, I heard that I had received funding to study for a doctorate in psychology, back at Keele University. My research was about eating disorders. I wanted to help increase understanding, and to improve the support offered to people who suffered from eating disorders. I established a support group for sufferers, and for their family members and friends. The meetings were encouraging, and the group grew in size, with about thirty people attending on some occasions.

As I met with people who were still trapped inside their illness, I felt very grateful to God for what he had done in my own life. I knew that I could have died when I was seventeen. Perhaps worse, I could have continued for years in the miserable prison of anorexia. Instead, I was happy and free. I tried to share some of the things which I had learned. I was aware that any of us could die any day, and I wanted to make every day count for God.

My time in Swaziland had whetted my appetite for travel. At the end of my first year as a postgraduate, I went to El Salvador for a month, through the Baptist Missionary Society 'action team' programme. I enjoyed being part of a team, as we tried to help in an orphanage and a school. There were some very sad moments as we encountered great poverty, but there were also many happy experiences, and we laughed a lot. One source of amusement was the mistakes I made when trying to communicate in Spanish. Confusing *hambre* (hunger) with *hombre* (a man) caused a delighted response!

In El Salvador, I had the dubious privilege of taking a shower with a giant toad, as my eyesight (without lenses) is so poor that I assumed it was a green sponge which was sitting by my feet! I also discovered what it is like to be awakened at dawn by a chicken biting my toes. Perhaps my most vivid memory is of the woman who had no money but told me, as she watched her children playing in the rubbish dump, 'We are rich because we have God'. I realised afresh how spiritual riches are all that really matter, and I felt humbled.

The following summer I had a rather different experience, as I went to Arizona. I had volunteered to help (and do some research) at Remuda Ranch, a Christian treatment centre for people with eating disorders. I was impressed by the way the centre operated. Treatment included individual and family therapy; teaching about nutrition; and groups which focused on many different topics, such as spiritual growth, relapse prevention, body image, sexuality, and expressing emotions through art or movement.

There was even equine therapy, which involved riding a horse through the Arizonan desert in the early morning. Initially I was sceptical about this, thinking that it was a gimmick to encourage patients to accept treatment. However, it didn't take long for me to see the benefits of this therapy. Each patient would ride the same horse every time, and many of the them who found it difficult to relate to other humans formed a bond of trust with the horse. As they groomed and cared for the horse, they were encouraged to look after themselves too. Some were initially afraid of the horses, and gained a sense of achievement when they conquered their fear and learned to ride. They were able to control the gentle but powerful animal, and were taught how they could gain control over various different aspects of life and give up the extreme control which they had exerted over eating and weight.

All this I could accept. Yet I remained dubious about the statement that staff tried to match the personality of the horse with the personality of the patient. For instance, a very unassertive patient would be given a horse which would do its own thing unless handled very assertively, while a patient who might benefit from expressing anger would get a horse which would bolt off in the wrong direction. I was encouraged to go with them one morning, and I was given a horse named Lightning. As I had never ridden before, I felt rather nervous. I need not have been. Lightning appeared to have an eating disorder, stopping to nibble every plant in sight, and going nowhere fast!

In Arizona, while I learned more about how to help people

overcome eating disorders, I also had a lot of fun, which was just as important for me. I even tried my feet at line dancing. I continued enjoying myself back in England afterwards, while I was completing my thesis. During my teenage years I had taken life very seriously. Since going to university, I had realised that Jesus joined in feasts as well as fasts, and wants us to enjoy life and to accept the good gifts which God offers us. I heard the saying, 'It's never too late to have a happy childhood', and this rang true. I felt quite liberated when I allowed myself to play like a child for a little while. That year I shared an office at the university with another research student, Dave, who was also game for a laugh. On one occasion, after a hard day's work, we whizzed down the empty corridors of the department in our swivel chairs. We also enjoyed playing on the swings and roundabouts in parks, and dancing round lamp posts. No alcohol was involved, just pure fun and love of life.

Dave and I played practical jokes on each other, using the internal phone system at the university. Once he disguised his voice well enough to fool me into thinking that the man on the line really was looking for help to overcome his eating disorder – until the anonymous caller said that his disorder involved eating motorway bridges! I managed to get my revenge during the summer, when I was working at an eating disorder treatment centre in Devon. I was expecting a call from Dave one evening, and I asked another staff member, Sue, to answer and explain that I was not able to come to the phone because my 'phone privileges had been removed'. Patients at the centre were occasionally told that they could not receive phone calls if they refused to eat (a policy which I did not approve of), and Sue explained to Dave that this had happened to me. Puzzled, he replied, 'No, it's Debbie the therapist that I want to speak to.' Sue replied in grave tones, 'I'm sorry to tell you this, but although Debbie has been pretending she is working here, she's actually a patient'. Poor Dave, not having known me for very long, fell for it, while we put the phone on hold and fell about laughing!

Although Dave and I got on increasingly well together, I convinced myself that we were just good friends. While I was anorexic, I had shied away from any friendships with men. Since recovering, I had developed friendships with several guys, but I had never had a boyfriend, and while studying for my first degree, I had vowed not to have one, at least until I was twenty-one, so that I would not get distracted from God. This vow came in handy when one of my male friends did ask me out, as I was able to explain why I could not accept, without his feeling personally rejected. Although I liked him, I was scared of entering a close relationship.

When I reached the age of twenty-one, and my vow 'expired', I spoke to God about renewing it – perhaps for a few years, or perhaps for life. As I prayed about this, I believe that God showed me that my vow was not something which I was doing to be obedient to him. Rather, it was a means of protecting myself from relationships, and possibly from rejection. God asks some people if they are willing to be single for him. I certainly was. I think God had a different question for me. 'Would you be willing to love a man, and perhaps even get married one day, if I guided you that way?' The thought made me cringe. Unlike many of my friends, I felt content being single. I valued my independence, and I believed it would be very hard to give that up and take someone else into account all the time. I liked to be involved with many people and activities, rather than focus all my energy on one man. What if he was disappointed with me, and wished he hadn't chosen me? Although I had come to accept myself, I didn't think that I would make a very good wife. For a start, I was hopeless at domestic tasks. If I couldn't make my husband happy, I would hate myself. I felt it would be better to remain alone. And what if I married someone who later turned away from God, as my father had? My father's apparent lack of interest in God was a constant source of sorrow to me, and I thought it would be devastating if I allowed myself to become really close to someone else, and then he also turned away from God.

In the back of my mind I hung on to the thought that if life ever became too painful, then, after my parents had died, I could volunteer to do humanitarian work in a conflict zone, where there would be a high chance of being killed. This fantasy gave me solace when I felt overwhelmed with sadness because of the suffering in the world. If I got married, I could not reasonably volunteer for this kind of 'death in service'. I would have someone else to live for, and I didn't think I wanted that.

Then there was the children issue. I felt that I would much rather care for needy people who were already alive than bring a new life into this troubled world. What man would ever understand that, and agree to forgo having children in order to support someone else's children? Even without children, marriage would involve sex, and that was something I still feared. So – surely God would not ask this of me?

I knew that God only wanted the best for me, and I knew that obedience to God was what mattered most in life. I agreed not to renew my vow of celibacy. But I told God that if he wanted me to go out with someone, he would have to make it very clear. If there was any doubt at all I wasn't going to risk it.

I carried on in blissful singleness until I was twenty-four, not at all disturbed by the fact that I had never had a boyfriend. Life was much simpler without one. I had several male friends, including Dave. Dave seemed so shy that I felt safe in the knowledge that he would never ask me out. People made comments when we started going to church together, but I just laughed them off. After one party, Dave and I walked back up the hill to Keele. I picked a fir cone off the ground, and presented it to him as a gift, solemnly pretending that it was a present of great worth. Dave picked a daisy for me in return. At the door of my flat, Dave asked me for a goodnight kiss. I froze. Was he still playing the 'let's pretend' game? Or might he be serious? Everything inside me hoped for the latter, but I wouldn't allow myself to think that. Not knowing what to do, I turned a reddened face towards Dave, and I stared at the ground. After what felt like a very long pause, he kissed me on the cheek. I tried to say 'goodnight' as if nothing had happened, but my world had started to change.

Even after this, I tried to persuade myself that Dave couldn't really be interested in me. He'd studied at Oxford University, and seemed much more intelligent than I was. He was such a great bloke – caring, gentle, honest, straightforward, and willing to talk about feelings in a way that few men did. I was sure he could find a better girl than me to go out with. He had never had a girlfriend, but as a teenager he had idolised one girl. I thought about the fantasy life he had built up around this beautiful girl with her long, fair hair and pretty dresses. If that was the sort of girl he wanted, what on earth could he see in me? I had taught myself that it was better never to hope than to hope and be disappointed. I kept trying to be rational with myself, as my stomach fluttered with excitement.

Dave and I grew closer as we spent more time together – working, relaxing, praying, cooking, eating, having fun, and talking on a deep level. Dave concluded that we were going out together, as we did the things that boyfriends and girlfriends did. He decided there was no need to actually ask me to be his girlfriend, as he felt we were past that stage. Had he asked me, I would probably have gently said 'No', as I was not 100 per cent sure that was what God wanted, and I had told God that if he wanted me to go out with anyone, he would have to show me. Perhaps God smiled as we became more than 'just good friends' before I realised what had happened! When I did wake up to the fact that we were going out together, I expected that Dave would quickly recognize that I wasn't good enough for him. In the meantime, I wanted to help him to feel loved and good about himself, as he too had been bullied as a child, and had low self-esteem.

I, in return, enjoyed Dave's love and care. Not wanting him to feel deceived, I also made it clear that I was never going to live up to his teenage fantasy of the ideal girl, and I wasn't even going to pretend that I could be perfect. At one of the meetings of the eating disorder support group, I played a song by Karen Carpenter (who herself had, sadly, died as a consequence of having an eating disorder). One of the group members had given me the song, as she felt it had a message for people with eating disorders. The chorus stated:

You've got to love me for what I am, for simply being me,
Don't love me for what you intend or hope that I will be,
And if you're only using me to feed your fantasy
You're really not in love, so let me go, I must be free.[1]

The song sparked off a discussion among the support group members, about their attempts to live up to other people's high standards, and their desperate effort to win the approval of parents and friends. They concluded that only God offered completely unconditional love, and that they did not want to spend their whole lives trying to match up to other people's ideals, or even the media image of a perfect body. Dave was also helping at that meeting, and later he and I spoke about our desire for our relationship to be 'real', and not founded on fantasy.

After completing my PhD, I moved to North Wales to train as a clinical psychologist, so that I would be able to offer therapy. The course involved a lot of work with patients, as well as written assignments, and I was kept busy. I loved the challenge, and the reward of seeing patients make progress. Over the three years of the course I worked with people suffering from alcohol abuse; autism; depression; eating disorders; obsessive–compulsive disorder; phobias; post-traumatic stress disorder and schizophrenia. I had a placement with children and their families, covering behavioural problems as well as emotional difficulties. I also worked for six months with people over the age of sixty-five, including those with dementia. Some of my work was with groups, including a drama group for people with learning disabilities, and an anger management group for people with criminal records. The job certainly had variety!

During the third year of my training, I became extremely busy. The clinical work was demanding, and in the evenings I had to work on my thesis. I was also on call at nights, as I was working as a night porter in a hotel, in return for free accommodation. Sometimes I received phone calls in the middle of the night and had to break the news to a guest that a relative in hospital had deteriorated and was close to death.

In my free time I was trying to help various people who seemed to be depending on me. I had several friends who were going through tough patches, including one who was psychotic and would phone me in great distress and confusion. I had been asked by a charity to act as a 'befriender' for several people with eating disorders, some of whom frequently phoned me when they felt like harming themselves.

During this year difficulties within my own family also became more severe. My mother took an overdose of tablets, and was taken to hospital where she had her stomach pumped out. She had a number of stays in a psychiatric hospital, where she was treated with one type of anti-depressant after another, to little effect. Eventually she received ECT (electro-convulsive therapy). This involves an electric current being passed through the brain, and is normally used only as a last resort in severe cases of depression.

I travelled from North Wales to Aberdeen at weekends when I could, to try to offer her some support. My father was spending the weekends with a new partner although he still shared a house with my mother during the week. My brother, who was training as a lawyer in Edinburgh, was a great support, visiting our mother frequently. She stopped eating for a time, and I would hold a cup to her mouth to encourage her at least to drink – she lost a lot of weight. At night I would lie awake listening to her scream for me to take her to hospital. I knew that it would not help if I did, and yet I hated ignoring her. Sometimes I gave in, and took her to hospital, where she demanded an injection of Valium to take away her pain. I felt torn with guilt, wondering if the strain of my anorexia years had been one of the causes of her breakdown. I also wondered whether I should give up my clinical training and go home to look after her, but I was always advised not to, as that would lead her to become dependent on me, instead of trying to get better. How I cried to see her in such pain. When I fed her and dressed her, I felt that I was mothering my mother.

Some weeks I spent more than forty hours travelling, as I was working in different locations and travelling to Scotland at weekends. Moreover, my older sister had now developed an eating disorder, and I felt very concerned about her. She did not want to tell anyone else, or to receive treatment. Although I knew that there was some evidence that eating disorders had a genetic component, I also felt that my anorexia had probably contributed to her difficulties, and I wanted to ensure that I did everything I could to help her.

I felt exhausted by all the demands on me. Under normal circumstances I would have turned to Dave for support, as he was my closest friend although he was still studying in Keele and so we only saw each other about once a month. Unfortunately, during the weeks when I felt under greatest pressure, Dave was also having a difficult time. He had generously invited a homeless person to share his university accommodation, and this had caused serious problems. I wanted to support him rather than to add to his stress, and so I chose not to tell him much about the pressure which I was under, although I did find it helpful to tell him a little about how I was feeling.

Although I liked to be independent and not to receive help, at times it felt almost too much. I felt like I was a single parent with two full-time jobs, trying to support a dozen children with emotional difficulties who were depending on me for help. I could feel the pain of those who were turning to me, and I suffered with them.

One evening, as I was praying, I saw a picture in my mind. This is very unusual for me as I don't tend to visualise things. I find it very hard to picture even people or places that I know well, and so I paid attention to this picture. In it, I was standing on a rock, surrounded by sea. There was only room for one person on the rock, but the sea was full of people who were looking to me to save them from drowning. I was holding someone with each hand, enabling them to keep their heads just above the water. I held them for long enough to let them regain the strength to swim again, and then I let them go so that I could help another two people for a while. Then I looked up, and saw that there was a helicopter hovering above, trying to lower a line for people to catch. Because everyone was looking to me, none of us had noticed the helicopter which was the only real chance of rescue.

As I thought about the picture, I realised that in real life I was depending on my own strength as I tried to rescue my mother, sister, friends and patients. I needed to learn instead to direct my attention to God, and see what he wanted to do in each situation. It was a great relief to discover that sorting people out was not my responsibility. After this I continued to offer people support, but I no longer felt responsible for rescuing them. I decided that I did not have to be constantly available to others which meant that I had more time available to develop friendships where I was not always in a supporting role. I realised that being self-sufficient was not necessarily a healthy thing, and I made a couple of appointments with a Christian counsellor, where I was able to off-load some of my own feelings.

Around this time I received a letter from my mother. Thinking that she was dying, she had written 'goodbye my love' on the envelope. I sobbed as I read it, realising that our relationship had become close through the pain which we had both endured. In the letter she said that she had always been careful not to show favouritism towards any of her three children. She explained that because I was always a 'dutiful daughter' (and so did not need to be told off), and because I was the youngest girl, she had worried that it might look as if I was a favourite child. She wrote that in order to prevent this, 'I think I over-compensated by being stricter with you than with the others'. She reminded me that I had been given the smallest bedroom in the house, which had been the only room without heating, where I had endured the cold Scottish winters without complaint.

I was stunned to read her words. I had assumed that if I was treated more harshly than my brother and sister, it was because they were more likeable. I had never imagined for a moment that my mother might be 'over-compensating' through fear of treating me more leniently! She ended the letter, 'I have always loved you all although I never said so enough, maybe because nobody said it much to me'. I determined to keep telling both my parents that I loved them. I wrote to thank them for various specific things which they had done for me, large and small, throughout my life. I also prayed that even in the dark depression that surrounded my mother, and was beginning to affect my father, they would be able to feel God's love for them.

In time, my mother started to show signs of progress, and my sister began to get help from a therapist. I completed my clinical training and Dave and I also managed to enjoy a holiday in Israel, where we completed a 200-mile sponsored bike ride in aid of a hospital. The hymn line 'my chains fell off' took on a new meaning for me.

While in Israel, I spoke with some missionaries who worked at the hospital which we were raising money for. Since childhood, I had wanted to be a missionary. I liked the idea of sharing God's love with people who were less well off than myself, and helping them in practical and spiritual ways. However, I felt that it was not right to go overseas long-term while my mother was ill. It seemed better to work abroad only for short periods. I was interested in finding opportunities to teach missionaries about stress management, mental health issues, and how to help both expatriates and local people who experienced depression or other emotional problems. During my final year of clinical training I specialised in working with missionaries and aid workers, and wrote my thesis on this topic. I also spent two weeks in Romania, providing training in counselling skills. I wondered how I might be able to keep up this interest after completing my training, as there seemed to be no jobs in this field.

As I approached the end of my course I accepted a job in Oxford, treating obese women. I felt compassion towards them, as I knew that many of them felt depressed and experienced self-hatred. I was keen to help improve the psychological treatment offered. Moreover, with this post I was offered one day each week to continue my work with missionaries and aid workers. I am still in the same job, and it seems ideal for me.

I have the opportunity to go overseas for short trips each year, to provide training for missionaries. On these trips I feel that I am an apprentice, trying to learn what I can, for use in the future. At the time of writing I am still in my twenties and I realise that I have a huge amount to learn. In my overseas work (for instance when working with people who have been evacuated because of death threats, or who live in war zones) I am especially aware that I need to rely on wisdom and strength from God, as some of the situations and cultures which I encounter are far outside my own experience. I don't know what is in store for me in the future, but I feel excited rather than afraid about the days ahead. I have a deep sense of peace, knowing that God is in control of my life.

While I was completing my training, I was looking forward to moving into a little flat of my own. I had been a student for nine years, living in various forms of shared accommodation, and I felt ready to have my own space. Shortly before I moved to Oxford, I went to a missionary conference where Tom Sine was the main speaker. I felt very challenged by his talks, and especially his emphasis on lives of community. As a result, I became willing to consider different accommodation options. I applied to live in a hostel for international students, as a member of a team befriending people from overseas. I had initially resisted the suggestion, but God knows best. I have lived in this community for the past two years, and at this point in time there is no place where I would rather live. As icing on the cake, Dave moved to Oxford last year, to begin training as a clinical psychologist. After years of a long-distance relationship, we now live in the same hostel.

My mother is now very well. She has moved to the south of England, and has become involved with many different activities in her church, as well as working as a volunteer in a charity shop. She claims that she is making up for the two years she spent in bed while she was depressed. As I write, she has recently been on a cruise, something which I would not have thought possible a few years ago. I have learned never to give up hope.

My father is also well, and is living with his partner in Scotland, and enjoying his retirement. My sister has made very good progress. My brother has managed to cope with the problems in the family without developing any stress-related difficulties himself. Although he is the youngest in the family, he has supported us all during difficult years, and has shown great loyalty. He has just become engaged to a lovely young woman, which has delighted us all.

In telling my story here, I have deliberately said more about my life since overcoming anorexia, than about the period of illness. One reason for this is that my life as an anorexic was very boring and predictable! A more important reason is that I want to show that there is life after anorexia. My identity is not as 'an ex-anorexic'. I get my identity elsewhere. While I had anorexia, the eating disorder was all-consuming, and I was hardly able to love. I tried to please people because of a sense of duty. Now I am free to love other people, and even to love myself.

I believe that complete recovery is possible. I'm now a normal weight, and my weight has been stable for years. I enjoy my food without worrying about weight gain. I tend to choose foods which are quick and easy to prepare, and inexpensive, but that is because I'm just as happy with these as with cordon bleu cookery, as I still do not have much of a sense of taste. I no longer centre my life around self-denial, and I have stopped punishing myself. I have managed, with God's help, to forgive myself, and also to forgive the people who hurt me in the past. I have become reconciled to my body. Where once I shrank away from touch, I now enjoy both giving and receiving hugs. The hugs don't break my bones – my bones have become stronger since I have been eating adequately (although they are still slightly on the brittle side as a result of the years of anorexia). In other respects, I am in very good health.

Since I've recovered I have enjoyed speaking at workshops and conferences, and on the radio and television. This is evidence that my confidence has increased greatly, because when I first went to university I was reluctant even to speak in a tutorial group.

Over the past twelve years since I recovered, I have experienced times of personal stress and the sorrow of bereavements, without ever returning to self-starvation as a way to help me cope with pain. Starving myself is not something I would consider. Nor would I turn to food for solace. I've learned how to face problems straight on, instead of using food as a coping mechanism. Of course I sometimes feel low, as most people do, but I realise that these feelings will pass. I can use my own weaknesses to help me offer compassion to others.

In my work with missionaries, I hear about some of the worst things that humans can do to each other – such as the atrocities which took place during the war in Kosovo, and the massacres in Rwanda. Hearing detailed reports of such events from eye-witnesses could lead to depression. I have learned to off-load the pain onto God, my heavenly supervisor, so that I do not try to carry it all myself. I also receive support from other people (including Dave), instead of trying to be self-sufficient.

Like many people with eating disorders, I used to be extremely concerned with what people thought of me. I would do almost anything to please. Although I still like to be thought well of, this desire is no longer all-consuming, as I know that God's view is all that really matters. Last week someone wrote me a note indicating that she found me insensitive, offensive, superficial and arrogant. In the past such words would have left me feeling intense self-hatred. But when I received this letter, although I felt upset that I had unintentionally offended the writer, my response was not to despise myself. Instead, I prayed that God would show me which of the criticisms pointed to real faults, and then help me to change. To assist in this process, I asked a close friend to help me discern which of the comments were true. Concerning the criticisms which I felt were based on misinformation, I forgave the writer, and wrote to ask her if we could speak together when she was next in Oxford, so that we could resolve the difficulties. Having apologised to her, if she still regards me with disdain, then I can live with that. My self-worth no longer depends on other people's opinion of me.

Neither does my self-worth depend on what I can achieve, or how much I can help people. Realising this has helped me to get rid of my unhealthy perfectionism. I have regained a sense of joy and fun and humour, and I make sure that I have time to relax and enjoy life. Recalling the picture of the rock in the sea, I remind myself that I am not the saviour of the world, and I do not have to spend every moment trying to help people. I know that Jesus offers me rest and a burden which is light (Matthew 11:30). I have learned that when the burden I'm carrying feels heavy, it is probably because I have picked something up which was not meant for me.

I am aware that there are always many useful things which I could do. There are always lonely people who might like a visitor or a letter; charities which are looking for more volunteers; opportunities to provide teaching and counselling; papers which could be written; situations to pray about, and so on. I also receive several invitations each year to teach in different countries.

As I already have a full-time job, I need to limit the number of extra tasks I accept so I try to let God govern my diary. I pray about what I should take on, and what I should not. I have found it helpful to realise that Jesus did not help every sick person he saw. For example, at the Pool of Bethesda there were 'a great number of disabled people' (John 5:3), but Jesus healed only one of them. While on earth as a human being, Jesus had limited time and energy. He asked God what he should do, and what he should not do. He even said 'no' to some direct requests. I am learning to do likewise, without feeling guilty.

I have a quotation from Henri Nouwen on my bedroom door, to remind me that my priority needs to be to spend time with God, and ask what he wants me to do. It reads:

> Try to give your agenda to God . . . Give every part of your heart and your time to God and let God tell you what to do, where to go, when and how to respond. God does not want you to destroy yourself. Exhaustion, burnout and depression are not signs that you are doing God's will . . . Once you have allowed yourself to experience [God's] love fully, you will be better able to discern who you are being sent to in God's name.[2]

This is one lesson which I think I will be learning all my life. I'm certainly not there yet, and I still make plenty of mistakes. Thankfully, I realise that I don't have to get everything right. I've discovered that it's OK to acknowledge my vulnerability. After all, I'm human. I know that I am loved and accepted despite my faults, and God is helping me to change. I am still learning how to listen to him. I'm learning to make more time to rest, retreat and be quiet in God's presence, moving away from the workaholism and people-pleasing which it is so easy for me to regress to.

When people say that they don't believe in God, I feel very sad for them, because of what they are missing. Some acknowledge that they haven't really looked at the evidence. As for me, I naturally look for alternative explanations and views; all my training demands that, and I have a researcher's mind, full of questions. Over the years I've considered different religions, and looked at the evidence for the claims of Christianity. Through looking, I've become convinced. My own experiences have added to my conviction, including miracles which I've had the privilege to see and experience.

Some people choose not to turn to God because they believe that would make life too complicated. It would involve a lot of change, and it's much easier to stick with the familiar. I can understand that. In a similar way, it's much easier to remain an anorexic than to recover. Recovery seems frightening. People who have anorexia often fear that if they recover they will lose their way of coping with life's problems, along with their sense of identity and the thing which makes them special. While ill, other people don't make many demands on them, but with recovery comes pressure to get on with life. There is also the fear that starting to eat more will lead to a loss of control over eating, and an inability to stop. Many people with anorexia feel trapped – not wanting to continue as they are, but terrified of what might happen if they start to change. Over the last ten years, through my research and clinical work, I have had contact with literally hundreds of people who either have eating problems or have recovered from them, and I have yet to meet one with an eating disorder who can honestly say that he or she is happy with his or her life. I have not met a single person who has recovered who regrets the fact that he or she no longer has an eating disorder, although the recovery may have been a difficult journey at the time. There are risks which are worth taking, including the risk of overcoming an eating problem, and the risk of turning to God.

Another risk which I found worth taking was the risk of making deep friendships. When I was six years old, my best friend moved to another school, and my mother taught me that it is better not to get close to people, as they can leave us. I lived without intimacy for years, and it certainly meant that I avoided the pain of separations. But I also missed out on some of the greatest joys of life.

I have discovered that life is full of risks. Becoming a Christian; recovering from an eating disorder; forming intimate relationships; getting married; becoming a parent: all of these, and many other stages in life, have costs attached to them. Taking the risk can lead to both greater highs and deeper lows in life. The joys of parenthood are accompanied by the sorrows of watching a child's illnesses, naughtiness and eventual separation from the parent. Marriage is made up not only of love, trust and partnership but also misunderstandings, different expectations, and the stresses of having to consider someone else in every decision. Friendship brings with it support, encouragement and intimacy but also the knowledge that your friends won't always be nearby, and won't always act in the way you want them to. Recovery from an eating problem brings great happiness, but involves taking responsibility in life, and often feeling worse before feeling better, as you fight against an illness which has distorted your mind as well as your body. Becoming a Christian means submitting your own desires to God's desires, and becoming his servant, in order to become truly free and fulfilled.

There is a poem called 'Risks', which I have seen printed in various places, always anonymously. It reads:

To laugh is to risk being a fool,
To weep is to risk appearing sentimental,
To reach out for another is to risk involvement,
To show feelings is to risk showing yourself.

To place your ideas, your dreams before a crowd, is to risk
    their loss.
To love is to risk not being loved in return.
To live is to risk dying,
To hope is to risk despair,
To try is to risk failure.

But risks must be taken,
Because the greatest hazard in life is to risk nothing.
Those who risk nothing do nothing, have nothing, and
    are nothing.

They may avoid suffering and sorrow,
But they cannot learn, feel, change, grow, love, live.

Chained by their uncertainties, they are slaves.
They have forfeited their freedom.
Only a person who risks is truly free.

In the parable of the talents (Matthew 25:14–30), Jesus described three servants who were given money by their master. The first two took risks, and used the money to make more. The third man was afraid of losing the money, and so he hid it in the ground until it was time to give it back to his master. He was strongly rebuked for that, while the other two received praise. What seems like the safest option is sometimes the most costly one, and it can mean that we miss out on what God wants to give us.

In the first few months after I had been in hospital with anorexia, I felt very ashamed that I had been anorexic and had caused my family so much stress. I was not willing to speak about it, as I was afraid of what people might think of me. It was six months later that I took the risk of responding to a newspaper article – as a result I was able to help others.

At a later stage, I felt almost proud to have recovered. When a friend said to me, 'I can hardly believe that you had anorexia', my immediate reaction was to feel sad that I no longer came across as thin enough, or as having sufficient will-power, to have been anorexic.

These days, I think that I have moved past the feelings of both shame and pride concerning the anorexia. It is just something which I went through in the past, although I'm glad that people who know me now find it difficult to believe that I was once anorexic. I do not like to boast about changes which have taken place in my life since I have recovered. I have tried to describe them honestly here, to give others hope, but I am very aware that it is only because of what God has done in my life that I am where I am today. If I'd been left to my own devices, I believe that I would have died as a teenager.

I look once more at the two women in my office. One seems without hope, but the other is full of hope, and looking forward to the days ahead. However black the situation may seem, 'with God all things are possible' (Matthew 19:26).

1. 'Love me for what I am' from the Carpenters' album *Horizon*. Words by John Bettis and Palma Pascale. Copyright © 1975 Almo Music Corp.(ASCAP) and Ars Nova Music (BMI).
2. H.J.M. Nouwen, *The Inner Voice of Love* (London: Darton, Longman & Todd, 1997) p 87.

2

An Introduction to Problems with Food and Weight

It seems that ever since Eve was tempted by a piece of fruit, and Esau sold his birthright for a bowl of stew, food has been an emotional issue. Biographies of St Catherine of Siena (1347–1380) describe her attempting to conquer her need for food, in the pursuit of spiritual holiness. St Catherine is said to have existed on a handful of herbs each day, and to have forced straw down her throat to bring up any food which she did consume. Her confessor tried in vain to dissuade her from the ritual. Her parents had attempted to force marriage on her, but could not break her control over her body, and she died at the age of thirty-three. She was just one of several medieval saints who lived in this way, and they have become known as the 'holy anorexics'. Like many anorexics today, these women were self-critical perfectionists, who were always ready to care for other people, but were unwilling to be cared for, counting themselves unworthy.

Between the sixteenth and the nineteenth centuries, there were reports of a number of 'fasting girls' who were regarded as 'natural wonders', as it was claimed that they survived without food. These girls did not claim to be fasting for religious reasons, but they were still perceived as 'miraculous maids', and viewed with great admiration.

Throughout the centuries and across different cultures, people have chosen to starve themselves. The majority of cases have been young women with low self-esteem, who have desired a form of control or independence. They have sought to succeed in a 'virtue' admired by society, whether this was holiness, self-denial or slimness.

The syndrome of anorexia nervosa was first medically defined in 1873. The name literally means 'loss of appetite from nervous origins'. This is a misleading term, as anorexia nervosa is characterised by extreme control of appetite rather than a loss of appetite. Nowadays, a diagnosis of anorexia nervosa is made if someone is at least 15 per cent below the normal weight for their age and height, and has an intense fear of weight gain. In addition, for this diagnosis to be made they must either deny the seriousness of their low weight, be unable to see how thin they are or have a self-evaluation which is unduly influenced by their shape or weight. In women who have been having menstrual periods, they must have missed at least three periods. The preoccupation with food, and the desire to avoid it, can take over every part of life – as in the case of the young woman who told me that she would not let her fiancé kiss her in case there were any particles of food in his mouth.

Self-starvation is not the only form that eating problems take, although others have received less attention. Binge-eating and self-inducing vomiting were practised in the early Roman empire, and so are not new behaviours. In AD 58 Seneca wrote of some of his contemporaries, 'They vomit to eat, and eat to vomit.' Nevertheless, it was not until 1979 that the first influential paper was written on bulimia nervosa.

The term 'bulimia' is derived from Greek words meaning 'ox' and 'hunger', or 'the hunger needed to eat an ox'. The condition is characterised by recurrent episodes of binge-eating. Binge-eating involves not only eating, in a discret period of time, more than most people would, but also feeling unable to stop or to control how much is eaten. It is as if something takes control of the people who are bingeing, and they simply can't stop eating. Even if they start choking, they might continue to put more food in their mouths. Usually people binge on food which is already prepared (such as bread, cakes, chocolate, biscuits or dried fruit) but this is not always the case. Some people plan a binge in advance and prepare food in anticipation. Others start to crave food without having anything suitable available, and so eat anything which comes to hand. In extreme cases, this might include food straight from the freezer, pet food, dried lentils or stolen food.

People who suffer from bulimia nervosa, like anorexics, evaluate themselves according to their shape and weight. After binge-eating they take action to try to prevent weight gain. For example, they might make themselves sick, abuse laxatives, diuretics, enemas or other medication, exercise excessively or severely restrict their eating. To meet diagnostic criteria for bulimia nervosa, there must be at least two eating binges a week (on average) for at least three months. Some people with bulimia binge several times every day.

Although some people with anorexia nervosa also binge and purge, most people with bulimia are of an average weight. Often their friends and family members do not know that they have an eating disorder; most people with eating disorders feel ashamed of their behaviour, and try to deny that they have a problem.

Some people binge-eat without making themselves sick or taking other action to prevent weight gain, although they feel distressed about bingeing. If they binge at least two days a week for at least six months, they can be diagnosed as having binge-eating disorder, the third of the eating disorders.

People with eating disorders use food (or starving) as a means of coping with problems, often by helping them to avoid thinking about their difficulties. All their attention is fixed on eating or avoiding food. Self-starvation can produce a sense of feeling distanced and even 'high'. Vomiting may also produce a sense of elation, and binge-eating can provide a temporary sense of comfort. In all of these cases, the disturbed eating pattern is a symptom of other problems. It acts like a pain-killer, to numb the sense of emotional torment and depression.

Many people have difficulties with food, or are preoccupied with their weight, but do not quite fit into any of the diagnostic categories. This does not make their difficulty any less significant. Some people do not binge, but 'graze' on food throughout the day, and feel very unhappy about their weight, or their apparent lack of control. They might define themselves as 'compulsive eaters'. While some people lose their appetite when they feel upset or anxious, others turn to food for comfort when they feel unhappy, bored, stressed, angry or tired.

Not everyone who is overweight feels distressed about their eating pattern or their weight. Some people simply enjoy food, and do not feel bothered about their weight. However, a considerable proportion of people in our society do worry about what they eat or how much they weigh.

Statistics vary, but it is generally accepted that at least 2 per cent of young women and 0.2 per cent of young men in Britain are known to suffer from anorexia or bulimia nervosa, while even more suffer from binge-eating disorder or consider themselves to be compulsive eaters. Among especially vulnerable groups such as dancers or models, at least 7 per cent have diagnosable eating disorders, while many more have 'subclinical' eating problems. In the UK, 13.5 per cent of men and 17 per cent of women are clinically obese.

Research indicates that by the age of eleven, over 50 per cent of British girls and 35 per cent of boys have taken measures to try to lose weight, or at least to avoid putting it on. These measures can be quite severe. For instance, they might eat only fruit and vegetables for a period of days or weeks; use their mother's 'diet pills'; start to induce vomiting; use laxatives or exercise excessively. In rare cases, children as young as five have been diagnosed as having anorexia nervosa. Comfort eating can begin even earlier.

Some surveys suggest that at any point in time around 60 per cent of British women are restricting their food intake in an attempt to control their weight. More than 90 per cent will regain the weight when they stop, ensuring that the weight concern continues.

These figures are true within the church as well as outside it. In fact, people with strong religious beliefs may be especially vulnerable to the extreme fasting and self-denial which can lead to anorexia nervosa. Other Christians comfort eat to hide their sorrows, instead of joining their peers who may cope by getting angry, swearing, smoking, getting drunk or acting promiscuously.

The apostle Paul wrote that, 'Food does not bring us near to God; we are no worse if we do not eat, and no better if we do' (1 Corinthians 8:8). However, many people consider food to have immense power and moral significance. They love it or hate it. It helps them to celebrate, or to commiserate. They see it as evil ('be a devil and eat some', 'OK, I'll be naughty'), or as a god which satisfies their needs. Another god is the bathroom scales, which determine how they feel. If they lose weight, they feel happy. If they gain weight, they feel depressed.

We live in a society where slimness is idolised. We are told that, 'you can never be too thin or too beautiful'. Models are envied, despite the fact that many of them engage in unhealthy practices to keep their weight artificially low. Self-starvation, deliberate vomiting, using laxatives, chain smoking and taking amphetamines are all considered a price worth paying to keep a skinny figure. Computer imaging is used to ensure that blemishes do not appear in fashion photographs. If even the models don't really look like that, what hope is there that anyone else will ever be able to? Little wonder that research has shown that women tend to feel more depressed, guilty and shameful after looking at pictures of models for a few minutes than they did before seeing the pictures.

At the other end of the weight spectrum, we find that overweight people are stigmatised. A number of studies have found that obese people, especially women, are less likely to be offered a job or promotion than slim people with the same qualifications. Obese people are perceived as being weak-willed, having poor self-control, and being more likely to have emotional difficulties than slimmer people. 'Fatty' is one of the first insults which is hurled around the school playground by young children. When shown pictures of children and asked which ones they would like to have as their friend, children routinely rate overweight children least favourably, preferring those with disabilities, those from different ethnic groups, or any other child. Even more disturbingly, in a recent survey 11 per cent of parents said that they would abort their child if they knew it was predisposed to obesity. It has been said that obesity is perhaps the last socially acceptable form of prejudice in the United Kingdom.

Huge amounts of money are spent on diet products each year. Many of them are completely ineffective (such as 'diet patches' which falsely claim to melt away fat without any change in eating pattern being necessary). People who are desperate to lose weight are willing to try almost anything.

We cannot blame the media, or society, for causing eating disorders, as that would be much too simplistic. Eating disorders are complex conditions, usually with multiple causes. There even appears to be a genetic predisposition towards weight and eating problems, especially obesity and anorexia nervosa. However, the value placed on thinness is certainly one factor which causes some people to starve, others to self-induce vomiting, and many to feel intense distress about their weight, and perhaps eat more to comfort themselves. Until recently anorexia and bulimia nervosa were rare in societies in which thinness was not valued. Sadly, these societies are gradually conforming to western standards of beauty, and eating disorders are becoming increasingly common all over the world.

Although everyone in our society is exposed to the message

that 'thin is in', not everyone develops an eating disorder. The people who are most likely to suffer in this way are those with low self-esteem. Those who develop anorexia tend to be strong-willed perfectionists, while impulsivity is common among those who binge-eat or eat for comfort. A desire for control may be important in maintaining anorexia. Many people with eating problems also suffer from depression, and their eating behaviour may be an attempt to relieve this. They may be unassertive and find it difficult to express their feelings, especially anger. They often lack intimate relationships with other people.

In a speech in 1993, Princess Diana explained that:

Eating disorders . . . show how individuals can turn the nourishment of the body into a painful attack on themselves and they have at their core a far deeper problem than mere vanity . . . From early childhood many had felt they were expected to be perfect but didn't feel they had a right to express their true feelings to those around them – feelings of guilt, of self-revulsion and low personal esteem. Creating in them a compulsion to dissolve like a disprin and disappear. The illness they developed became their shameful friend. By focusing their energies on controlling their bodies, they had found a refuge from having to face the more painful issues at the centre of their lives.

It is important to remember that every case is different. This will be seen in the chapters which follow. Anyone can develop an eating problem, whether they are a princess or on the dole; a professor or someone with learning disabilities. They may come from any ethnic group. Although anorexia tends to peak around the ages of fourteen to seventeen years, bulimia in the early twenties, and binge-eating disorder and compulsive eating later on, the people who suffer from these conditions range in age from children to people over seventy. Between 5 and 10 per cent of sufferers are male. Eating disorders are sometimes discussed in the media, especially when the sufferer is well known. What many people do not realise is that thousands of people suffer secretly with eating problems; in some cases, no one else knows about their struggle, not even their parents or spouse.

People with eating problems may suffer quietly for many years, feeling ashamed and disliking themselves because of their eating habits. Some people move from one type of eating problem to another. Others live on with the same difficulties, year after year. Others die. Anorexia nervosa has the highest mortality rate of any psychiatric condition. Studies which followed up people with anorexia nervosa a few years after they received treatment found that 5 to 10 per cent of them had died. Generally about half of the deaths are suicides, with electrolyte imbalance or the direct effect of starvation causing other deaths. Bulimia nervosa may also result in death due to suicide or electrolyte imbalance (as a result of laxative abuse, or vomiting. Few people realise that using laxatives and inducing vomiting can lead to life-threatening problems. They are also ineffective methods of weight loss, as laxatives take effect *after* food has already been absorbed, while vomiting tends to cause subsequent overeating). Obesity is associated with an increased risk of heart disease, strokes and diabetes.

So much for the sombre side. Thankfully, this is not the full picture. While up to one third of those with eating disorders never recover, but struggle on year after year, another third make significant progress. They overcome their eating and weight problems sufficiently to hold down a job, perhaps sustain a marriage, and generally enjoy life. When they go through difficult times (such as bereavement or relationship problems), they tend to revert to using food as a coping mechanism, but after the stress passes, they continue to cope reasonably well. They do not claim to be totally free from their weight concerns. They are not completely relaxed around food, and they continue to worry about their weight more than most people do.

Nevertheless, they feel that they have made a lot of progress, and are generally content.

The final third are even more encouraging. These people progress to a stage where they feel completely free of the eating problem. They can enjoy food without being obsessed with it, and it no longer holds any power over them. They maintain a normal, healthy weight, and are not preoccupied with their weight. They accept themselves, have close relationships with other people, and are emotionally healthy.

The sooner someone receives help to overcome an eating problem, the more likely they are to fully recover, but it is never too late. I have worked with people who have struggled with eating disorders for more than thirty years, and yet who have gone on to recover. One of the keys that opens the door to freedom is actually *wanting* to recover. For some people, the disordered eating pattern has become their identity and they cannot imagine being any different. It is central to their life, and they don't know who they would be without it. It is their friend and comforter. People with anorexia nervosa may believe that their low weight and control over food is the only thing that makes them special. Those who eat to block out their emotional pain may feel that food is their only source of comfort. In order to begin to want to change, it can be helpful for these people to list both the pros and the cons of their eating problem.

Imagine a parent who has been told that it is in their best interests for their child to be taken away from them. The child is a drain on their finances and their energy and is making them very tired. Their thoughts are preoccupied with the child, and they are not free to do the things they used to do; they are tied down. They can no longer be spontaneous or suddenly decide to go abroad, or even to go out to a party and they worry about their child, which is not good for their own health. However good and true the arguments are, few parents would be willing to give up their child!

Likewise, some people with eating problems are unwilling

to change, despite the knowledge that their health and social life and perhaps their finances are suffering. They will not be willing to give up the problem until they have replaced it with something else. For some people, there is an unhealthy 'trade in'. One eating disorder may give way to another, or to alcoholism, or workaholism, or excessive exercise, or self-harming behaviours. Other people replace the eating problem with more helpful ways of coping. Some learn basic skills of problem-solving, and then manage to face difficulties and decisions directly, instead of using food to escape from them. Some become more assertive and are helped to build up their self-worth, so that they no longer choose to punish themselves. Some find a sense of achievement, control and fulfilment in their work. Some find a true friend to replace their friendship with food or starvation. Some learn to express their feelings through music, art, dance or writing, instead of hiding them. Some discover that God loves and accepts them just as they are, unconditionally, and forgives them completely – and they move to a place of deeper healing and wholeness.

Many people with eating problems have asked me how others recover from anorexia or bulimia, or overeating difficulties. I am also asked how the friends and family members are affected, and how they cope. This book contains testimonies of women and men who have recovered from a variety of eating problems, in some instances after suffering for decades. There are also chapters by people who have supported a family member in their recovery. Each person was helped in a different way. Their testimonies show that full recovery is possible. They are stories of hope. As the logo of the charity Anorexia and Bulimia Care states, 'There *is* an answer'.

People with eating problems generally feel ashamed about their difficulties, and keep them a secret. The honesty of those offering these testimonies is a sign of how much they have changed.

Key steps forward in the path of recovery include admitting

that there is a problem, wanting to overcome it, believing this is possible, and replacing the eating problem with something more adaptive. The chapters in this book illustrate additional factors which may help to promote fuller recovery. Each chapter is written by a Christian, who has found their faith to be of importance in the healing process. Those who are not Christians can also recover, but many people say that their Christian faith helped them to recover.

The road to recovery can seem a long road, and there may be 'roadblocks' and wrong turns along the way. Those who refuse to give up when there are problems, but see them as experiences to learn from, will keep moving forward and get there in the end. However small the step, if it's in the right direction, it is worth taking. Do not despise the day of small things (see Zechariah 4:10).

When I ran a support group for people with eating disorders, one of the women who came along brought the following 'autobiography' with her. I think it is true to the experience of many people:

An autobiography in five short chapters

Chapter 1
I walk down the street.
There is a deep hole in the sidewalk.
I fall in.
I am lost.
I am hopeless.
It isn't my fault.
It takes forever to find a way out.

Chapter 2
I walk down the same street.
There is a deep hole in the sidewalk.
I pretend I don't see it.

I fall in again.
I can't believe I'm in the same place.
But it isn't my fault.
It still takes a long time to get out.

Chapter 3
I walk down the same street.
There is a deep hole in the sidewalk.
I see it is there.
I still fall in.
It's a habit.
My eyes are open.
I know where I am.
It is my fault,
I get out immediately.

Chapter 4
I walk down the same street.
There is a deep hole in the sidewalk.
I walk around it.

Chapter 5
I walk down another street.
(Portia Nelson)

The accounts within this book are not intended as a replacement for professional help. I encourage people to seek such help, if they feel able to do so, in addition to trying any approaches which are described here. This is especially important in cases of anorexia nervosa, due to the very serious health consequences posed by this condition.

The first point of contact is usually a General Practitioner, who is able to make a referral to an appropriate professional who can help the individual to move forward. Research indicates that the treatment with the best results, at least for people with bulimia nervosa, is cognitive behavioural therapy. This can be provided by a clinical psychologist or another professional trained in this approach. It involves changing the thought processes ('cognitions') which maintain the eating disorder, as well as changing behaviour. This approach is also helpful in cases of anorexia nervosa and overeating problems. Some of the chapters which follow describe how this approach can help. Further information about treatment options, and other advice, can be obtained from the organisations and books listed in the Appendix.

To people who are reading this book because they want to help someone else who has an eating problem, I would like to say a sincere 'thank you'. Your love, support and willingness to listen may help your friend or loved one to feel valued, and this may give them the strength to make changes. Caring is more important than knowing all the answers. 'They won't care how much you know, until they know how much you care.' Nevertheless, I hope this book will help further your understanding of eating problems, and give true hope for recovery. The organizations listed can give you further guidance, should you want it.

Knowing what causes eating disorders can help us work towards preventing these conditions from developing. Anorexia and Bulimia Care (ABC) runs a prevention programme in schools, and would be happy to provide information about this. One fifteen-year-old girl who was recovering from anorexia asked me to pass the following message on to any young person who might be tempted to experiment with extreme dieting, laxative abuse, vomiting or other such behaviours:

Nowadays, having an eating disorder is almost considered 'trendy'. I think magazines and TV almost encourage young girls to starve themselves, to achieve the so-called 'perfect' body, which will not, and cannot, ever look like that anyway. But they don't actually tell you the true effects that starving yourself can have.

You become obsessed with doing everything possible to burn calories. Every spare minute is used to do aerobics or jog. Your mind becomes totally occupied with calculating how many calories and grams of fat everything contains, and also how you can avoid any meals. You become very deceptive and your life is based around lying to people about how much you've eaten, when and where, and constantly hiding food, and planning tricks of how you can hide food. The only books that interest you are cookbooks and looking at pictures of food and planning out huge meals, which you can only dream of eating. You spend hours walking up and down the food aisles in supermarkets, working out calories. You can't concentrate on anything, be it school-work or watching TV, because all you think about is food. You start to lose interest in your friends and withdraw, and you feel uncomfortable in large groups, because you think that everyone else just sees you as a body, and what's more, a fat body! So you stop going out at all and just stay at home, usually exercising or studying.

You cause your family a tremendous amount of pain – my parents feel that they have failed, and have been so tense that my mother has to take pills to stop her hair from falling out, and my father has to wear protection over his teeth at night, because of migraines from grinding his teeth together. My sister has become very resentful towards me, because she doesn't understand why I'm committing a slow suicide, and whereas we used to be very close, we now hardly ever talk. Your body doesn't get the nutrients it needs so your skin and hair go really dry and lose all their shine. Your nails become brittle and break. Your periods stop and you lose all interest in the opposite sex, and looking good and going out and having fun. You start growing horrible fine hairs on your back, and you're always cold. It becomes painful to sit for too long or to sit on a hard chair or even to have a bath as your bones stick out so much. You only wear big, baggy clothes because you feel so self-conscious and want to hide your body.

Because I had to go to a psychiatric ward for five months, I missed so much school-work that I had to repeat the year. I've lost virtually all of my friends, because I withdrew from them so much that they felt neglected and thought that I didn't want to be around them any-more. Nobody knows how to act around me and everyone is scared that they're going to say, or do, the wrong thing.

I just wanted to tell you that however trendy it may seem, dieting to achieve the perfect body is not going to make you happy, or give you any fulfilment. You are hurt-ing yourself not only physically but also mentally, and causing all those around you, who love and care for you, a great deal of pain. It's just not worth it!

The eating disorder is not worth it, but the person who has an eating problem is worth a great deal. Recovery is also worth it. However hopeless a situation may seem, recovery is possible, as the following accounts show.

Recovery from Compulsive Eating or Binge-Eating Disorder

Yvonne – Expressing Feelings, and Choosing to Forgive

I grew up in a family where food was a big issue. I suppose that if I'd lived with a family of alcoholics I might have turned to drink. But it was to food I turned to ease any pain or stress which I experienced. I learned to eat when I felt upset, as it made me feel better for a while.

My father was in the merchant navy, so he wasn't around much. I was brought up in a house full of women – my mother, my aunts and my grandmother. They were constantly on diets, but they didn't seem to lose any weight. They felt guilty about eating. I'm sure that they used to secretly binge-eat, but that was something which nobody ever spoke about. I didn't even realise that bingeing was abnormal. I thought it was something which everyone did. It was only later, when it started to make me very ill, that I realised it was an odd thing to be doing.

I was a very slim child so I was an object of interest to my relatives, as none of them were slim. My mother equated love with feeding. She never restricted our food, and we were encouraged to eat as much as we liked. She was pleased if we overate. When I was about fifteen, I started to diet, even though I didn't need to; I don't know why I started – it was just something that all the women in my family did. I suppose you can always find some bulges on your body when you're developing, if you look hard enough. I noticed that my hips and my tummy were getting a bit bigger, so I dieted.

I suffered from a digestive problem for quite a few years while I was a teenager which was probably stress-related. The illness made me lose a lot of weight, as I wasn't able to eat much. As I recovered I was encouraged to put the weight back on, but once I started eating more, I found it difficult to stop, and I felt that my eating was completely out of control.

My teenage years went by in a bit of a haze. I yo-yoed between losing weight through dieting and illness, and then eating compulsively. Looking back, it seems one big muddle – a roller-coaster of losing weight and then regaining it, but at the time, it was just how life was.

I started my first job when I was eighteen. All the girls at work were dieting, and I tried to join in; I would start the day with good intentions, but by lunchtime I would give up. I got into the habit of consuming large amounts of chocolate during the lunch hour, as I was very unhappy at work and the chocolate helped to make the day bearable. I could quickly devour a one pound bag of pick-and-mix, or a big box of chocolate peppermint creams.

My weight went up by around two stone at this point, to about nine stone. Although this might not sound much, it was heavy for me, as I had always been very petite and slim. I'm only five foot three, and I'm very fine-boned. After I had gained this weight, two of my school friends saw me on a bus one day, and argued about whether or not it was me, saying, 'It can't be, she's so fat'. I would probably have gained even more weight if I hadn't been so active. I couldn't drive in those days, so I walked a lot – to and from work, and to the shops and back, carrying all my shopping. Later, I started to compulsively exercise as well. I once walked to the next village, eight miles away, and then turned round and walked straight back.

I got married when I was twenty-five. Before this, I had always had food set in front of me. After the wedding, I was able to choose what I wanted to eat. My husband was very, very thin. I asked him to have a health check, to make sure that he was all right. The doctor confirmed that he was OK, but said he needed feeding up, because he had not been eating properly while he was a student. I didn't know much about nutrition or healthy ways to help someone gain weight, so I bought him lots of chocolate, cake and biscuits – I bought them for him, but I could not resist them. The compulsion to eat was unbelievably strong. If someone had tried to take food off me, I think I would have scratched his eyes out. I would eat what I had bought for my husband, and then I would buy more to replace it before he even saw it. I would eat the replacements too, and again buy more. My husband did manage to get to some of the food before I did, and he slowly gained weight to a normal level. By then my eating was completely haywire.

I convinced myself that I wasn't eating much, because I never ate a proper meal. But I was eating all the rest of the time, even when I was walking around. I always ate standing up. I would binge on a whole pie or a flan. I also ate massive amounts of chocolate. I worked as a librarian and I would eat Twix bars on the way to the library, more at lunchtime, and then on the way home. Once, I tried to eat *enough* chocolate to satisfy myself – I ate until I was physically sick, and I still wanted more. I thought then, 'There isn't such a thing as *enough* chocolate.' That was quite a frightening thought – I couldn't stop eating, even if I wanted to.

When my husband was away on business, I would live on biscuits, sweets and chocolates for a couple of weeks. I used to shake a lot. I think it was a miracle that I didn't get some kind of sugar disease or diabetes.

My eating problem became worse and worse, until I was in my late twenties. Then my health completely broke down. I'm sure my eating habits did not do my digestive system any good, and I started to feel constantly unwell. I felt emotionally exhausted; I would get terrible panic attacks; my hair fell out, and I had awful skin trouble. My body would swell up with water. It was quite dramatic; I used to make great pits in my skin by pressing my thumb into my legs. Sometimes I couldn't bend my legs because they were so swollen. I was really a mess. I felt extremely depressed, but then I think anyone would be if their hair was falling out, they were covered in spots and swollen up!

I was very good at covering up, and I don't think other people were really aware of my difficulties. I never had time off work, even when my hands were so swollen that I couldn't bend my fingers. I was very stoical, I would never give in to anything.

At home, I cried a lot. Sometimes I would have terrible rages over trivial things. If my husband had forgotten to do something, I would explode, and slam doors and bang around. He must have wondered what had happened to me. I finally plucked up the courage to admit to him that I had a problem with food. He didn't fully understand the compulsion, and he said, 'Well, just try and stop.' It was around Christmas, and he was going out somewhere. There was a box of peanuts in the house. I waited for him to go out of the gate, and then I started cramming nuts into my mouth. To my horror, he popped back for something which he had forgotten, and he caught me emptying the box of peanuts into my mouth. He tried to stop me. I beat him off, so that I could go on cramming nuts into my mouth. That's when he realised that I had a serious problem.

I shared my husband's opinion that I should be able to simply stop my compulsive eating. I never sought professional help about it – although I realise now that professional help can be highly effective. I did see a doctor about health problems which were caused by my eating patterns, but I felt too ashamed to mention my compulsive eating. I tried telling a couple of friends about what I was going through. They didn't take it very seriously, because I wasn't extremely fat. They thought that I was fortunate to be able to eat so much and not get terribly fat. They didn't realise that what I was doing was very painful, and was destroying my life.

I considered attending an Overeaters Anonymous support group meeting. I phoned the person in charge of the local group, but I came off the phone feeling worse instead of better. I think she was still suffering quite badly from eating problems herself. She was eating while she was talking to me, which was very unnerving. She was also an untreated alcoholic, and she sounded unsympathetic and unhelpful. I set off for the meeting, but when I got halfway there I turned round and came back. I decided it might cause me more problems, rather than help me.

I tried time and time again to stop bingeing, but my attempts never succeeded for more than a few days. I resigned myself to living this way for ever.

There are whole blocks of time which I just don't remember. It's as if I was on some kind of tranquilliser. I was sedated with food. I didn't have much of a social life, I was quite isolated, as my eating problem was a secret which very few people knew about. I couldn't enjoy meals out, like other people did. I would never let myself feel hungry, so I would always eat so much before a social event that my appetite would have disappeared before I got to the meal. I never enjoyed food, I used to cram it into my mouth so quickly that I didn't taste it. It was meaningless, it was horrible.

In retrospect, I am very aware that God was with me all the time. Even when my suffering was at its peak, I never questioned his presence or care for me. I had been sent to Sunday school from the age of five. My parents never went to church and really weren't Christians at all, although they would have felt very insulted if anyone had said that to them. My grandfather was a Catholic, and I probably absorbed his strong faith from texts that were on the walls and things he said. As I grew up, I chose to believe in God and I prayed. I prayed about my eating problem, and this gave me strength to keep going.

I'm convinced that my prayers were answered. One especially vivid answer came at a midweek church meeting which I attended after one very, very bad day with food. The speaker announced that she was going to abandon the talk which she had prepared, because she felt that God wanted her to tell us about how he had helped her when she had struggled with overeating. I knew that her message was for me, and after the meeting I shared my difficulties with her. We prayed together, and she encouraged me to hand the whole situation over to God. We physically held our hands out, and asked God to take the problem. In the past I had said to God, 'Come and help me.' This time I was saying instead, 'Here is my problem, I hand it over to you.' It sounds like a subtle difference, but it's a very important one. In the past I had asked God to be with me, in the midst of my problems, and he had done that. But this time I took the problem and gave it, completely, to God. I was left with the effects of my eating behaviours. But somehow the problem was diminishing.

My behaviour started to change even on the way home from that meeting, when I told a close friend what had happened. She was very supportive. Just telling another person, who didn't dismiss it as 'not a problem', helped in itself. She had experienced psychological difficulties too, and so she knew what I was talking about. I became a lot calmer, but I still ate compulsively. I was disappointed that I was not instantly cured. Looking back, I can see that God was healing me, but was doing this slowly so that I could learn many lessons along the way. In particular, I think he wanted to show me the reasons behind my compulsive eating, so that he could bring me to a deeper level of healing.

There were many, many times when I said, 'I'm going to stop today', and tried to stop my compulsive eating. But I never managed to stop a binge halfway through, or to wrench myself away when I felt desperate to binge. It is possible to delay eating for a while, by using your willpower to take you away from the situation – for example, by going out without taking any money so that you can't buy chocolate. But you haven't really recovered if you just do that. You are simply an overeater who hasn't got any food, and as soon as you have access to food, the problem is likely to emerge again. You could be locked in a room for a month and so not be able to overeat, but that wouldn't mean you were cured. For me, it was important to discover the reasons for my overeating.

I was in my early thirties. My eating patterns had been bizarre for more than fifteen years, and I had a very strong desire to be normal. I wanted to be like people who could eat half a bar of chocolate and then wrap the rest up and put it in their pocket. It seemed amazing to me that people could do that – that they could have a packet of sweets in their bag for days and just eat one now and then. I desperately wanted to be like that.

One lunchtime I was in Bristol shopping centre, cramming Bombay Mix into my mouth. It suddenly dawned on me that I didn't even like the taste of it, and I didn't want it. I thought, 'I don't even like this stuff, why is my hand reaching into this bag and shoving it into my mouth?' I felt as if there was a force controlling me and making me do something I didn't want to. It was really odd. I thought, 'Isn't this funny?' I was able to stand aside from myself. I decided, 'I'm going to investigate this, this is interesting.' That's when I started to observe myself and question why I was behaving in such a peculiar manner. I began a process of self-discovery.

I'm a very independent person, so I went through this process on my own. First I looked at my behaviour in detail. Then I started to read. I was a librarian in a university medical library, so I had easy access to books. I read books on psychology and books about compulsions – not just eating, but also gambling and alcohol. I read books about counselling, and I began counselling myself. I read anything which I thought might help me glean a little insight and I felt that God was guiding me in the books which I read. Sometimes I picked up obscure looking medical textbooks. Time after time I found that something inside them helped me in my recovery. I knew that whatever book I was reading, God was in there with me. Sometimes I would read a whole book and just find one little phrase which really struck home.

I had terrible acne, so I studied dermatology books to look for reasons for it. One phrase in a book jumped out at me. A doctor stated that he thought acne could sometimes be a symptom of suppressed rage. I thought, 'Yes! That's exactly what it feels like. There's some rage suppressed in me.'

I started to question, 'Why would I be angry?' I thought back to my childhood, and to when my eating problems began at fifteen. That should have been an age when I was forming opinions of my own. However, my mother had been so frightened that I was striking out on my own, that she had clamped down even harder. I had contributed heavily to this myself, as I had been very submissive and easy to control. I think that my family members saw me as a weak person who needed to be told what to do. They thought that I didn't have any opinions or ideas of my own, as I never voiced them. I had felt dominated, and unable to express myself. I felt that I was not given any respect. I had felt angry, but I had not expressed this anger, because we were never allowed to; to be angry was to be very wicked.

I realised that my eating problems tended to be worse when I got into situations where I felt that I couldn't control what was happening to me. Taking orders at work was not too bad, but when people started telling me what I should and shouldn't be doing in my personal life, I would overeat. I didn't have the confidence to stand up for myself or express myself, so I would turn my anger in on myself, and I would eat furiously.

It wasn't just other people bossing me about that used to irritate me. I was bossed about by myself as well! I wouldn't allow myself to be mediocre, I had to be the best. Everything I cooked had to be spectacular. When I'd had a few successes,

I couldn't allow myself not to be so successful the next time, so I was always trying to be better and better. Gradually I realised that this was silly, and that nobody would mind if the food I served them wasn't perfect. I started to question my standards, and as a result I changed my outlook on life. It's easy to say this, but it took years.

My husband gave me the support which I needed as I made changes. His patience seemed without limit, and he helped build up my self-confidence. He didn't appear critical, even when I behaved very strangely. I found this amazing, because if our positions had been reversed I think I would have felt very annoyed, and demanded that he stop bingeing. But since the episode when he found me devouring a box of peanuts, he knew that it wasn't that easy. He was always sympathetic, treating me as if I was suffering from an illness. I was such a misery most of the time, it must have made his life very unhappy.

It would not have helped if he had tried to lock food away and wrench the problem from me. That would just have made me feel more panicky. He knew that the real problem wasn't greed or a lack of self-control. He helped me to look at myself and consider what was going on.

My husband had known my mother, and so when I told him about my anger concerning my childhood, he knew what I was talking about. That was a great help, because I could bounce ideas off him. We would talk for hours, and sometimes I broke down and cried. Occasionally I would receive a letter from my mother which seemed just too annoying, and I would run round the house screaming, which was a great release! That got it out of my system. Knowing that my husband understood me and that my anger was being received by somebody, without judgement, was a great help.

I don't blame my mother for my problems. I went through a phase of hating her for the way she had treated me; but then I started to think about why she might have treated me like that, and I realised that she had her own problems, and her own messed-up childhood. My grandmother was a wonderful woman, but she was also very controlling, and this seemed to have been passed on from generation to generation. I tried to think myself into my mother's position, and I started to see the situation from her point of view. I realised that she had always done what she thought was best for me. I forgave her for hurting me – I knew that she had never intended to do that. If she had realised, she would have been devastated. You can't really blame somebody for doing something by accident.

Some books imply that you must talk to the person who has made you angry in order to make progress. But this is not always possible. It takes two to talk, and I couldn't have confronted my mother about this. She would have thought that I was blaming her and criticising her, and she would have started crying, and felt destroyed. Instead of confronting her, I had long conversations with her in my head, and I made her reply in the way she would have responded if she hadn't been so messed up herself. I tried to strip away the muddled part of her, and talk to her 'inner self', and we sorted it out that way. So, we had conversations without her knowing it. I needed to recognise the problem, forgive my mother, and learn to deal with stress in more constructive ways.

My husband and I often talk about the fact that I am a different person now to the person he married. I've become much stronger and wiser, and that permeates my whole life. The main thing I've learned is to know myself and how I'm feeling. I've learned to talk about my feelings and to express them, instead of trying to escape from feelings by sedating myself with food. I don't allow people to impose their opinions on me anymore. I don't argue back all the time, but I let their opinions wash over me if I don't want to accept them. I've learned that it's OK to say, 'No, I don't want to do this', or 'I don't agree with you', or 'I'll do it my way thank you very much', rather than thinking that I always have to do what somebody else has suggested. It is impossible to do everything, and I needed to learn that I could choose which tasks to accept, and when to say 'no'. Saying 'no' was one way in which I learned to express myself and my own opinions, instead of being dominated by other people.

Some Christians think that assertiveness is unbiblical, and that we should be meek and mild and compliant. But assertiveness was very important in my recovery, and I believe that Jesus was assertive. He was able to say 'no', and as I have learned to do that, as a result, I feel totally different. The suppressed anger has gone. I'm known as a very calm person now. I believe that I am now more self-aware than many people, and because of this, I am better able to help others. People bring their problems to me because I can always see two sides to a situation. I have stopped blaming myself for events in the past, and I have taken responsibility for my life and my future. I feel assertive, happy and confident, which is the complete opposite of how I used to feel. I also feel powerful in the best possible way – not in an aggressive, dominating way, but in a way which encourages other people to feel powerful and confident as well. Previously, I behaved like a child. Now I am more mature.

Moving further away from my family helped me to become my own person. I moved house a number of times. Each time, I was so busy packing and unpacking and sorting out new jobs that I didn't have time to binge. That in itself jolted me out of some of my bad habits.

My eating problems began gradually and I recovered gradually, but all in all I suffered from them for about twenty years. I've been recovered for over fifteen years now. As I started to express myself more, I felt less need to binge; eventually my bingeing faded out almost unnoticed. I now maintain a weight within the normal range for my height. I rarely weigh myself, as I don't want to be obsessed with my weight.

I would say that I eat normally now. Looking at people around me, I think I'm more normal than they are! When you actually observe people, it seems that most women in our society have got some concerns about eating. It fascinates me when I notice other people feeling guilty when they eat a cream cake or some biscuits, or feeling proud when they refuse them. I think, 'Either have it or don't have it, but don't make it such a big issue!' It amazes me that I was once a million times worse than that. Now I'm totally at ease with food. I can eat slowly and savour and enjoy food, which is something I never used to do. So perhaps I'm not normal, but I'm what I think normal should be! I eat very regularly, very healthily, but I'm not obsessed with it. On a day-to-day basis, I'm not that interested in food. That's another funny thing, because I used to spend literally whole days cooking. I was an obsessive cook, creating elaborate meals for other people; now I just do the bare minimum. I don't pore over cookery books, or spend hours shopping for food, like I used to. Usually I just prepare meals as a routine part of life. I make them as nutritious and as nice as possible, but after eating I get on with life, without thinking any more about the food. Food is not invested with great emotional significance for me any longer. Again, this came as a gradual change.

When I think about the way I used to live, dragging my swollen body from binge to binge, it seems like a horror story. There were times when I seriously contemplated suicide. I used to look at happy people and envy them, but never in a million years would I have dreamt that one day I would be one of them. I was in such a deep pit, I could never have got out of it without somebody reaching in and picking me up. The most wonderful thing I have learned is that whatever kind of pit we fall into and however deep we go, God will always be able to reach down and get us out of it. This doesn't just apply to eating problems, it applies to any difficulty we might face. It can sound almost trite to say that there is always hope, but I know it is true. I was in a very, very bad state, but now I am more normal than many people who have never had an eating problem!

It's good to be able to look back on my experiences. Even

people who have not completely recovered yet benefit from looking back and seeing how far they have come, because it is easy to forget how far you have travelled. As I look back on my own path of recovery, I can say that I wouldn't have wanted to miss this episode in my life, because I don't think I'd be half the person I am now without it.

4

Louise – Challenging Unhelpful Thoughts

I was born forty-four years ago, into a family which could be described as upper middle class. My parents, and especially my father, approached life with a 'stiff upper lip', rarely showing any form of emotion. My father worked long hours as a solicitor and saw very little of us during the week, not getting involved in the general day-to-day upbringing of his four children. My mother stayed at home and looked after our physical needs very thoroughly, but emotional needs were not discussed.

My two elder brothers were sent to boarding school, which they loathed. I went to an exclusive, private all-girls school, where competition was rife. Girls at this school either pursued academic success, sport or boys. I chose the latter. There was also a lot of competition regarding who was the slimmest. Because I didn't have much confidence in my academic ability, I channelled all my energy into slimming, and choosing the right clothes and hairstyle, in the hope of winning approval in that way. By the time I was thirteen years old, I had become very concerned with my weight. I found that I could be better at dieting than most of my contemporaries. I weighed about eight and a half stone at the time and I am 5 foot 7 inches tall. I swung from rigid dieting to binge-eating and then using laxatives in the hope of preventing weight gain. Thus began thirty years of eating problems.

I was seriously underweight by the time I was eighteen. My

weight crept up a little, but then fell once more. When I was twenty, I was diagnosed as suffering from anorexia nervosa. I was using slimming pills, which were readily available at that time; I also took Valium and sleeping pills, so I was quite 'drugged up'. When I was offered hospitalisation in a psychiatric ward, the suggestion shocked me, and in order to avoid it, I decided to try and gain weight on my own.

At this point my boyfriend, who was a lapsed Christian, went to America for three months to work and see friends. When he came back he told me that his Christian commitment had been 'revived' while he was away, and he kept talking to me about Jesus and my need for salvation. I resisted this quite strongly until eventually one day I felt that I couldn't resist the truth any longer. I didn't really want to become a Christian, but I could not deny the existence of God. And I knew that I could not sort out my life myself. I had not even managed to gain weight by myself. Although I had tried, my weight had dropped to just six stone. I turned to God, cried a lot, and I know God heard and intervened. That was a dramatic turning point in my life. Nothing was quite the same after that – becoming a Christian was, and continues to be, the central focus of my life.

My problems did not suddenly disappear. In fact, I spent the next two days crying constantly. I think this was due to at least three things: God was doing some important work in my life; I had given up the tight control over food which I had held for so long; and my body was suffering from extreme malnutrition and could not take much more.

After my conversion, all my resolve to starve myself seemed to vanish, and I started eating again. It wasn't that I decided that I must, it was something which just happened. I think that this was God intervening, because if I had carried on refusing food for much longer, I would have become very seriously ill.

Having started eating again, I found that I could not stop, and I rapidly gained weight. I had completely lost touch with feelings of hunger and fullness, as I had overridden those sig-nals for years. I began to binge-eat every day. I only stopped eating when there was no room for a crumb more. I never made myself sick, I just waited until I began to feel that there was space inside me for more food. As soon as I started to feel any-thing other than completely full, I would top up with another binge. My stomach had shrunk while I was anorexic, and it was absolute agony to force in as much food as I did, but I felt com-pelled to do it. I was now a compulsive eater.

Unlike some people who shop in preparation for a binge, I would grab anything I could get my hands on. Sometimes it was sugar that I wanted desperately, and sometimes fat; usual-ly it was both. On some occasions I filled myself with dried fruit, and sweets, and biscuits, and honey straight out of the jar. At other times I would consume half a tub of margarine, half a pound of cheese and pints of milk.

Every time I binged, it felt as if the world had come to an end. As I was bingeing nearly every day, this was hard to endure. The pain and discomfort of eating so much food was crippling. The mental torment was even worse. I would tell myself that I hadn't just failed in terms of controlling my eat-ing, but that I was useless at my job and had failed in every area of my life. My thinking would be completely negative. As soon as the darkness lifted a little, I would start tormenting myself all over again. Large portions of my time were spent in these black glooms, when nothing good could show its face at all.

After about six months of serious bingeing, my binges became less frequent, until I was bingeing just once or twice a week. I would try to compensate the rest of the week by not eat-ing very much. I would eat too little, then binge, then eat too little again, yo-yoing up and down.

My weight doubled, from six stone to twelve stone, and people wondered what had happened. I didn't like being twelve stone, although other people did not generally make com-ments. I attended a couple of self-help groups, and while I found them to be companionable, I don't really think they aided my recovery.

Something which I did find helpful, was identifying some of the causes for my eating disorder, even though I wasn't able to do anything to change them. Up until this point, I had tended to criticise myself for my eating problems, and to tell myself that I was a horrible person because of my difficulties. When I was able to understand some of the reasons for my difficulties, I began to stop blaming myself.

My doctor, who was a Christian and knew me well, was very helpful. He referred me to a psychologist, who offered me cognitive behavioural therapy (CBT). This form of treatment focuses not just on the problematic eating behaviours, but also on the thoughts and ideas (cognitions) which maintain them. I learned to catch myself when I had unhelpful thoughts about food, body image, weight or myself. Previously I had accepted without question thoughts such as, 'I can't control what I eat', and I had responded by eating more. The thought that I was horrible and useless went unchallenged. Now I learned that it was possible to identify unhelpful thoughts, and ask myself questions such as 'Is it true?'. I practised replacing unhelpful thoughts with more helpful ones, and found that my behaviour and my emotions changed as a consequence.

I read some very useful and practical Christian books on this topic, such as *Telling Yourself the Truth* by Backus and Chapian. This book helped me to understand that the disciplining of thoughts is a biblical principle, and something which everybody should do, even people who have not got particular behavioural problems.

Before this, I would just let my mind wander on, even if my thoughts were destructive. Through speaking with the psychologist, and reading, I discovered that I could choose to think differently. I learned to quickly identify any negative thoughts which I had, and to answer them back with positive statements. I found this to be very helpful, even if it did involve talking to myself! I reminded myself of biblical truths, including that I am made in the image of God (Genesis 2:27), and 'I am fearfully and wonderfully made' (Psalm 139:14).

Challenging my unhelpful thoughts made a huge difference in all sorts of areas of my life. My self-image improved as I started to see myself as God saw me. The book *Overcoming Overeating* by Hirshmann and Munter also taught me some important lessons about self-acceptance. I started to tell myself, 'I love myself too much to binge today.' To stop bingeing forever seemed like an impossible task, but by making healthy decisions on a daily basis I was able to move on, and make major changes in my life.

I learned the importance of accepting myself as I am now, rather than saying, 'I'll accept myself when I reach a certain weight, or have achieved various goals.' Yesterday has gone and tomorrow will look after itself; change begins with where we are today. I started to acknowledge that God loves and accepts me as I am, and on that basis I love and accept myself as I am. The more I came to accept myself, the more I felt at liberty to enjoy life. I told myself that no one else cared what shape I was. If people only loved me because of the way I looked, they wouldn't be worth knowing anyway. I knew that if I could accept myself just as I was, the battle would be won.

As I started to value myself, I began to try to deal with my feelings in appropriate ways, instead of turning to food while ignoring my real needs. I used to binge for just about any reason. If I was depressed, anxious, cross or cold I would eat to provide a sense of release. I learned to identify the triggers which led me to binge. When tempted, I tried to determine whether I was really physically hungry (in which case food would do me good), or if I was reacting to a negative event – such as having a row with my boss, or falling out with my children, or having a tiring day or a bad night, or feeling ill. I learned that I did not need to binge because I felt angry or upset. I told myself, 'If I'm cold, eating isn't the answer; if I'm sad, eating will make it worse', and so on. I practised dealing with my emotions in a more appropriate manner.

Perfectionism and rigid rules regarding eating had also led me to binge-eat. I used to count every calorie I consumed. If I had eaten more than 400 calories by mid-afternoon, I felt this was dreadful, and this usually led me to binge. I would think, 'I've done it now, I've had 450 calories, I've blown it anyway so I'll just continue eating'. I would then go on and eat 3,000 calories on top of the tiny bit I had already consumed. Calorie counting had a big effect on my mood but never helped me to eat less when I was overweight, so I stopped doing it.

I had a lot of 'thou shalt not eat' rules which I had built up for myself, forbidding me to eat anything with sugar or fat in it, or anything which wasn't low in calories, high in fibre, and fresh. Of course, I couldn't always keep the rules. When I broke them I felt out of control, so instead of just eating one slice of cake, I would eat the whole cake, and lots of other things as well. Having strict rules set me up for failure, and when I failed I broke all the rules and ate everything which I usually deprived myself of. I gradually learned to stick to a sensible, balanced diet without classing any foods as 'forbidden'. I allowed myself to have treats from time to time, without feeling guilty.

I needed to do a lot of 'unlearning'. It seemed that every magazine I opened suggested tips on dieting. Every time I turned on the TV I saw advertisements for low calorie food. Dieting bombarded me wherever I went. I found it helpful to avoid reading articles about dieting, and to steer clear of all the fad diets which promised sudden weight loss. When I was feeling vulnerable around food, I avoided watching cooking programmes on TV, or doing any baking, as that would have made it even harder to resist the temptation to overeat.

Whatever you feed your mind on influences you. People who read pornographic literature find their thoughts and behaviour influenced by it. Likewise, reading about diets, and then reading recipe books about chocolate cakes, led me to eat the chocolate cakes and then try to go on a diet, making me obsessed with eating and dieting. People who are vulnerable in this area find that reading a lot about it can feed the problem. In order to change, I trained myself to say, 'I'm not going to think about this' when I found myself thinking obsessively about food and weight. I would make a definite decision to think about something else. If I caught myself wondering, 'What do I weigh today – did I put on weight after what I ate last night?' I taught myself to respond, 'I don't have to think about this, it's boring, there are many other things which I'd rather think about'. I learned to switch to thinking about something more constructive.

Our society seems to be obsessed with body image and shape. I am now able to see how unhealthy this obsession is, and I choose not to engage in it. I think 'the perfect body' is a complete myth. I have discovered that many of the models and film stars who are portrayed as having ideal bodies go to very unacceptable levels to maintain their low weight. Very few of them are naturally that thin. Some of them take drugs, some are bulimic, and others swallow tape-worms in order to keep thin. The camera can also lie, and make them look thinner than they really are. Most of them can't sustain their low weight for any more than their peak of five years, and most models, once they give up, put on weight. Before I discovered this, I would look at them and think, 'That's the way I want to be'. Now I know that it is not worth paying that price. I no longer think that I'm a failure just because I don't look like them. There is a genetic contribution to weight. People who fight against their predisposed size have to fight all their lives. People are not thin because they are clever. They are either naturally predisposed to thinness, or else they are doing something which is damaging to their health to keep them that way.

I know from experience that people with eating problems can read every book on the shelf, but until they decide they really want to overcome the problem, and work out a viable strategy, nothing will change. Recovery takes effort, but there is no magic answer. You can receive prayer and all sorts of support, but unless you have the will to change, and are willing to put effort into it, you are unlikely to recover. You can hope things will happen and wish they would happen, but sometimes you have got to make them happen. The decision to eat or not to eat is obviously within yourself. People can try to make you change, but that just makes matters worse.

I believe that I have only been able to overcome my disordered eating patterns with God's help. My binge-eating habits were deeply ingrained. It is only because people were praying for me, and because I decided I wanted to change and I was willing to work at recovery, that the impossible became possible, and I managed to recover.

I believe very strongly in the power of prayer and the ability of God to intervene in my everyday life. I prayed about all the aspects of my eating disorder which I could think of. People prayed with me about the eating itself. This was helpful, although it was not a magic wand to suddenly make me better. Rather, there were lots of steps along the path to recovery. I had to work together with God to change deeply-rooted habits and to transform my way of thinking. I also prayed with people about the depression I had experienced, and about my family, and about various negative relationships which I had been involved in. I dealt with each problem as it arose.

Other Christians gave me a lot of support by listening to me, praying for me and sticking with me. I strongly believe that if God had not intervened in my life when I was twenty, I would have continued losing weight and probably have died. I could see no way out of my problems. My salvation was the turning point in my life, and while it did not herald the end of my eating disorder, it heralded the beginning of the road to recovery.

I have received professional help at various times when, although my eating has improved, life has become stressful and

I have wanted extra support. It has been useful to receive a bit more therapy, to help me get my mind telling me the right things again. I don't see this as failure, I see it as a growth process, which goes on in leaps and bounds throughout life.

In times of stress, I can still be tempted to react by overeating. I have to work at keeping my thinking right. I weigh myself once a week, to check that I don't become overweight again, as people who have been overweight are at risk of regaining weight. If I checked my weight more often than that I might become too obsessed with it. Weight fluctuates anyway, so weighing myself more often would be senseless.

I now have a positive outlook, whereas before I was in a black hole. I have learned to work out what I want to eat, and to allow myself to enjoy that. If I feel that I want to treat myself to something special to eat, I try to identify exactly what it is that I want. If I think 'What I really want is white chocolate Lint', then the chances are that when I've eaten that, I'll feel satisfied. If I try to make do with a banana instead, I am likely to eat the banana and then think, 'No that wasn't what I wanted', and then I'll have something else, and in the end I'll have the chocolate anyway. So it is better to have what I really want in the first place, and to allow myself to savour it, and thank God for it. Enjoying food doesn't mean I'm greedy, it means that I'm listening to my body. I don't feel guilty about doing that.

Looking back, I feel that if I had sought psychological help much earlier, I could have made a quicker recovery. But at that time I regarded psychiatric help as indicating that you should be in the 'looney bin', and I wanted to avoid it. I think that there is less stigma attached to such help nowadays. An eating disorder is just a type of illness, like any other illness, and I would recommend that anyone with a serious eating problem seeks professional help. One-to-one help is preferable, as everyone has different reasons for developing their problem, and different ways of getting out of it. I think that people who are able to work through their problems with a professional in this field are more likely to get well and stay well than those who try to press on alone.

Nowadays I eat very reasonably most of the time, although once in a while I eat more indulgently. The times of indulgence are not like the binges I used to have in the past. I used to condemn myself if I ate more than I had planned to. I would feel so bad about myself that I would think, 'What can I do to feel better? Eat.' That perpetuated the problem, and the guilt I felt would push me to eat even more.

It was a real revelation to me when I discovered that most people in our society overeat from time to time, to some degree or other. It's normal to do this sometimes. For instance, I have noticed that my husband (who is a man of average weight, with no food problems) will seriously overeat now and again, if at a barbeque or wedding or party. It doesn't bother him at all. He'll say, 'I feel a bit full,' but he won't say to himself, 'What a disgusting person I am, I had six puddings' – the way I would have spoken to myself. He might say, 'I did have six puddings, they were jolly nice, I feel full now so I'll skip supper.' I used to think that everyone else was 'law abiding' when it came to food, and I was the only 'criminal' who broke the rules and ended up overeating. Now, if I eat more than I intended to, I consider this as a sign that I am normal. Eating more than I need from time to time prevents life being too bland and boring, and is not really a problem. My way of thinking has completely changed. I have let go of the thought that I must be perfect and never overeat. I am much kinder to myself now, and I set myself realistic goals.

I now maintain a stable weight, and I perceive myself as slim and toned. I am not unhealthily thin, and I am certainly not fat any more – I am fit and healthy, and eat normally. I enjoy exercising, using an aerobics tape for half an hour each morning, except for Sundays when I give myself a day off. People sometimes ask me how I stay slim. There's nothing new and nothing magic, the answer is simply that I eat sensibly and exercise regularly.

More importantly, I have found a deep level of self-acceptance and stability in my life. I have a loving husband who has supported me faithfully through the ups and downs of life. We have two healthy children, both miracles of God's grace as I had severe infertility problems as a result of years of abusing my body. I have come to see that there is much more to life than physical appearance, and that it is 'who you are' not 'what you look like' that matters.

I would like to encourage other people with eating problems to believe that there is a way through, and to never give up. I recovered after thirty years of eating disorders, and other people can as well. If you have found something that helps you, such as counselling, it is worth sticking with it, even if progress seems slow. It is important to be honest with yourself. Sharing your feelings with other people who understand can be very helpful.

Those who are helping someone who has eating problems need to be patient, and to keep feeding in positive thoughts and ideas, with sensitivity. Recovery is a long-term business, and it is important not to have unrealistic expectations. Nagging about eating habits tends to make matters worse. The real battle is in the mind, as habits change when thinking changes.

5

Shelley – Praying in a New Way

Looking back, I feel that I had to cope with quite a lot during my childhood. The family home was very unsettled. My father drank a lot, and was often verbally and physically abusive to my mother, brother and, to a lesser degree, myself. As a result of this, conflict also developed between my brother and I, and between my mother and I. Family life was fuelled by fear and criticism, although we were very close in our own way, and despite the negative emotions, there was also a lot of love within our family. But somehow it all seemed very destructive. I often had to protect my mother or brother physically from my father. I took on too much responsibility, and although I had some good friends, I felt quite lonely and insecure. My parents kept splitting up and talking about divorce, and then getting back together again, which added to the insecurity.

As my brother grew older, he also became volatile and quite violent, but in my mother's eyes he could never put a foot wrong. He had little ambition, and he often got into trouble both in and out of school. My mother and grandparents appeared to accept that this was just what boys did, but my father seemed to resent him further for this.

We were the 'black sheep' of the larger family network, and unfortunately we also seemed to be less academically endowed. To make up for my felt deficiencies, I tried hard to keep up with my cousins academically, and to prove my worth within the family. Despite all my best efforts, I received much criticism, and I always felt inadequate, except for my physical appearance.

On one occasion I was sexually abused by an elderly uncle, but this was swept under the carpet by the family. Again, this made me feel that I didn't really matter.

On the outside I was happy-go-lucky, a survivor, and I prided myself on my ability to 'bounce back'. In reality, I had very low self-esteem. From an early age I often felt sad, and I frequently thought about suicide. When I was seventeen, my father finally left home. Two days later, after a row with my mother, I moved out as well, and rented a house with another girl.

As a child, I did a lot of exercise and we were taught to eat healthy food – high-fibre, low-fat meals. Chocolate, chips and other high calorie foods were seen as special treats. After I left home, I began to turn to these treats for comfort when I felt lonely or sad. I would get a box of chocolates and a bottle of wine, and curl up in front of the TV to watch a film on my own. I might have some fish and chips as an extra treat. It soon became a pattern that if I felt down, insecure or tired, I would comfort eat.

After I left home, I began to train as a nurse. My boyfriend and I had been together for six years; this relationship providing most of my security. We talked of marriage and long-term commitment, but the relationship remained unstable. I became pregnant, and had an abortion. At the time, I didn't think that the abortion had affected me in any way, as I felt I had made the right decision and had not embarrassed myself or my family. Not long after this, I broke up with my boyfriend and even though I was the one who had decided to break up the relationship, I felt devastated.

I found it difficult to sustain new relationships because of the chaos which I felt. I moved into accommodation for nurses and I found another boyfriend, but again, although we loved each other very much, our relationship was very rocky and volatile.

I spent two years going in and out of hospital for abdominal pain, queried ectopic pregnancies and pelvic disorders. My consultant was unable to find a reason for my difficulties.

Eventually he diagnosed constipation, and recommended that I increase my fibre intake, and drink more water. Feeling desperate, I blurted out that I was unable to eat a normal, healthy diet; my eating consisted of bingeing on high-carbohydrate foods. Because of my upbringing I was only too aware of the nutritional values of foods, and I knew that my diet was far from balanced.

The consultant was taken aback by my outburst, and asked 'What do you mean?' I found it difficult to be honest about my eating pattern, as I felt ashamed of it, but I tried my best to explain, and as a result, he referred me to a counsellor.

As I was living away from home, I didn't have friends or family around to support me, and I found it difficult to cope with the issues which arose during the counselling sessions. I also found it difficult to talk about these issues, as I felt people didn't understand, and didn't really want to hear. By spending all my time thinking about food and eating it, I could ignore my emotions and take my mind off my problems – I didn't have to 'feel my feelings'. Food was my means of comfort, and an escape from emotional pain. My eating habits got worse. I would go from shop to shop buying pies, chips and boxes of chocolates, eating £25 worth of food at one sitting. I could spend all day going from shop to café to takeaway, and then trying to sleep because I felt too unhappy to remain awake. I was completely out of control. There were times when I ate so much that I couldn't keep it down. At times, I made myself sick, or exercised to try to burn off the calories, or took amphetamines for slimming purposes. I was desperate not to gain weight. My family had always focused on my appearance and, as I felt very insecure and inadequate in other areas, it was important to me that I could look good and gain control in the area of my weight. This helped me feel better about myself.

I sometimes went to visit my mother at weekends. When I did, I went along to a church near her home. I had gone to Sunday school when I was younger, and I sometimes prayed. I believed in God, and in Jesus as he is described in history books. One day the pastor at the church spoke about 'meeting Jesus Christ', and afterwards I asked someone what this meant. He asked if I would like to meet Jesus. I imagined that he meant having a physical encounter with Jesus, rather than a spiritual one. I thought I would close my eyes and be able to visualize Jesus standing in front of me. I said yes, I would like that. He then prayed with me, asking Jesus to meet with me. As we prayed, it felt as if I was being introduced to the person who was going to be my best friend and relieve me of my worries. I didn't *see* Jesus, but I felt that he was with me, and I was sure that he was going to remain with me forever. It was definitely a shock to the system, although it was a very pleasant one.

Having been introduced to Jesus during this time of prayer, I then had to go on and develop my relationship with him. Before, I had only known Jesus through books. Now I wanted to know him personally, as my friend. It was a bit like forming a relationship with anyone. The more time I spent talking to him (in prayer), and listening to him (through reading the Bbile), the better I felt I knew him. I felt different in myself, like a new person. I also felt a bit confused. It was as if I were also getting to know myself all over again, as this new friendship changed how I saw myself.

As I started to grow as a Christian, I became more aware of what was going on within myself, and I realised the extent of my eating problems. I had been good at denying that I had any real problems. I had been a hyperactive child within a disordered family, and so I had never really known what 'normal' was. I started to claim, 'Ever since I've become a Christian, my life's just fallen apart.' That wasn't really true, but God began to show me my hidden feelings and insecurities, so that he could heal me. My difficulties and symptoms, which I had tried to black out for so long, became more evident. I began to regret things which I had done in the past, especially the fact that I had chosen to have an abortion. I wished that I could turn the clock back. Had I listened to my heart at that time, instead of to my head, things could have been so different.

When I became a Christian I wasn't told what to expect, nor was I given further teaching, and I struggled with my faith. I didn't understand much about Christianity, and I was living in a non-Christian environment. Because I felt lonely, I often returned to my old lifestyle, which centred around nightclubs, drinking and sex. I lived in a 'work hard, play hard' environment, which allowed me to drift on from day to day without really thinking about what I was doing. Little by little, over the years, God taught me how he wanted me to live, and helped me become more whole.

The counselling which I was receiving helped to raise my awareness of what I was doing, and the consequences of my binge-eating. Knowledge alone did not help, however, as I felt completely unable to stop myself. I could not walk home from a counselling session without spending more than I could afford on food. I ate compulsively. Food ruled my life, and I felt trapped and helpless.

As I did not feel that the counselling was helping me to change, I was referred to a cognitive-behavioural therapist. I chose to go to this therapist for three reasons. Firstly, I had read that cognitive-behavioural therapy was the most effective treatment for eating disorders. Secondly, I believed that the therapist would begin by helping me to find ways of controlling my behaviours. Talking about my thoughts and feelings was relevant and important, but the focus had to be on changing my behaviour. If it was less out of control, my feelings and thoughts about my worthlessness might automatically decrease. Thirdly, I knew that the therapist was a Christian, and I hoped I would be able to talk with him about my spirituality as well as about my eating behaviour. I also felt that I could trust him more, because he was a Christian.

I was referred to the therapist via my doctor, and so I did not have to fund myself. Tim, the therapist, began by listening to me. I felt that he understood my spiritual needs, to a degree, and he was quite supportive in that respect. He also provided practical suggestions of how I could control my behaviour. The theory was that using certain strategies would help me to break the cycle of bingeing. In particular, Tim encouraged me to write in a diary three times a day, recording the triggers for my behaviours and the consequences of them. We then talked about the sorts of things which triggered me to binge-eat. We discussed the patterns which emerged, and ways in which I might be able to change them. Just voicing these patterns to somebody else made me more aware of them. My destructive behaviour had come to seem almost 'normal' to me, but through discussing it, I was able to realise that it was not normal. The desire to change became stronger.

Tim suggested that I should plan in advance what I would eat each day. He explained that if I was too strict with myself, I would set myself up for failure, which would lead me to overeat again. He recommended that I allow myself a treat every day. He also helped me to challenge my thought processes, in the hope that this would help sustain my recovery. Although this therapy helped to some extent, I continued to binge-eat. I was often distraught, and I spent evenings in tears. I hated my body and I detested myself.

The following twelve months were the worst months in my life. Every time I began an eating session and I realised that I was out of control, my self-hatred would increase. I would feel very angry and eat faster and more aggressively, as if I was punishing myself by making myself even fatter. I would eat more and more, even if I didn't like the food, thinking, 'I might as well just eat it, I'm a total waste of space'. I no longer made myself sick. I didn't have the energy or the motivation to care about exercising any more – even to walk to the shop was a big chore. I often thought about harming myself physically. Occasionally I scratched myself superficially, but my better judgement always seemed to take control at that point, and I would realise how I was behaving, and make myself stop.

It felt as if I was bingeing twenty-four hours a day, and was piling on weight. I felt completely out of control, and it seemed that I had lost the energy to fight against it. I often planned to take my own life, and one evening I decided to go along with these plans. I took an overdose, and washed the tablets down with a bottle of wine. At the last minute I panicked, and phoned a friend. I was taken to hospital and had my stomach pumped. It was at that point that I decided I could never do that again, and I had to just take one day at a time, focusing on God.

At this stage of my life, I felt in such despair that I would have said that I was not getting better at all. I could only remember the bad days and the things which went wrong, and I paid little attention to the progress I made and the times when I managed not to binge. Looking back, I realise that this was all part of the recovery process. I needed to be healed gradually, layer by layer, like peeling an onion, as I walked through different issues in my life.

One ray of hope which flickered in the darkness was that I could feel that people were praying for me. Gradually, I did take little steps forward, and the bingeing became less frequent. I tended to feel better after going to church, even though no one really understood what I was going through. I believe God put in my path people who would help me and be there for me, accepting me in the mess I was in. This really helped. Being able to pick up the phone and chat or cry to my mother was another lifeline.

I still felt guilty about having had an abortion, and so I spoke with somebody who had taken a similar course of action. She prayed with me, and I came to realise that God had forgiven me. The next step was for me to try to forgive myself and although I found this difficult, gradually I was able to, although I still regretted my actions.

Every year a group from my church went off to a Christian

conference, known as 'Grapevine'. I enjoyed going, and I received spiritual refreshment there. It was a time of wonderful fellowship, as well as being a good social event. The third time I attended, I asked a member of the Grapevine team to pray with me. They asked if I had received the spiritual gift of being able to 'speak in tongues'. I said 'No.' Although I knew that not all Christians could speak in tongues, and that it was not the most important thing, I had felt somewhat inferior to those of my friends who did have this gift. The team member prayed that I might receive it, and then encouraged me to open my mouth and try speaking in tongues. I found this very strange and initially I could only say one word. I was told that this was OK, and that God would develop this gift in me if I allowed him to do so. This indeed took place, and I was thrilled.

Some time after the conference, I went into a shop. It was about eight o'clock in the evening, and I had come out of the nurses' home with the explicit purpose of buying food to binge on. I was on a self-destruct mission. I felt divided in two. One part of me really did not want to binge, and the other part was totally out of control, and desperate to binge. I walked in and stared at all the goodies. I was like a crazed woman.

Suddenly, instead of picking up chocolate as I usually did, I found myself praying in tongues. I felt that I was praying for guidance and help. The desire to binge completely left me. I had gone into the shop to select the most fattening foods which I could find. I walked out after buying just one low-fat yoghurt and some bread, which I could eat sensibly. I felt that I was walking on air. It was brilliant, God had enabled me to resist the temptation to binge! I praised him all the way home.

This experience was repeated a number of times. Before this, when I had felt a craving to binge, I had believed that there was nothing that I could do to resist this urge. Even praying (in English) had seemed futile when my desire took over. Now I discovered that by praying in tongues, I could focus on God and not on my desire to binge, and God could give me the strength to walk away from the temptation. Sometimes I gave in and binged, but more and more often I found that by turning to God for help, he provided the strength I needed to resist my obsession.

It says in the Bible that the Holy Spirit, 'helps us in our weakness. We do not know what we ought to pray for, but the Spirit himself intercedes for us with groans that words cannot express' (Romans 8:26). I believe that God provided the words for me, and by doing so, helped me to overcome the desire to binge.

Although the bingeing eased, I still felt insecure and unsettled. My nursing training involved having placements in different parts of the country, and I moved house ten times in three years. I did not feel that I belonged anywhere, and I felt very isolated.

Around this time I realised that my stepbrother, whom I had been very close to, had become emotionally dependent on me. I was unable to meet his emotional needs as I felt so weak myself, and I began to feel smothered. I spent six months feeling annoyed with myself for causing him pain, and confused about my own emotions. I seemed to have ended so many relationships by hurting other people and confusing myself, and I wondered if it was better not to get involved in close relationships.

Towards the end of my training, a man named Andrew joined the small church group which I attended. He and I got on very well; we had a lot in common, both in terms of experiences which we had been through, and also our feelings. We appeared to think alike on many issues. We bonded immediately, and I was relieved that we seemed to be able to be good friends, without any romance. We went to church and to the gym together. Andrew seemed to understand me and accept me and I felt very relaxed in his company. He used to phone me at odd times, just to see how I was and to chat, and I did the same for him. Although he couldn't comprehend my eating behaviour, he showed that he cared for me. He provided support and he loved me just for the person I was, not expecting me to live up to any standards. As the relationship developed, my desire to binge lessened, because my emotional needs were being met by both God and Andrew.

After two months as the friendship developed, we started going out together. After another two months, due to different circumstances, we both had to leave the separate hostels where we had been living. We decided to get married, which we did within two months.

Marriage has helped to slow me down and stabilise me. Andrew and I are very happy together, and we have just had a baby daughter, who is a great delight. My relationship with my mother has been strengthened, and I am now able to love and forgive my family.

I suffered from an eating disorder for five years. Since I have recovered, I have had times when I have been tempted to place too much emphasis on food again, but gradually this has happened less and less, and now it is not really an issue. When I feel that I would like to eat chocolate, I go and buy one or even two bars, and enjoy eating them. By allowing myself to enjoy some of what I want, I've found that I can stop after a bar or two, instead of eating twenty more, as I used to. The compulsion to binge has left me, and even the thought of it makes me feel sick. I realise that I didn't enjoy food when I forced bar after bar of chocolate down my throat, not even tasting it. That was like an addiction. It was an attempt to squash my pain and loneliness for a short while. Food is not the answer to such problems.

Nowadays I generally eat healthily, and I allow myself a treat, however minor, every day. I'm able to enjoy the good things which God has made. He has brought me through from self-hatred to self-acceptance, and from hating life and abusing myself to enjoying life and looking after myself. I'm very thankful for that.

Recovery from Bulimia Nervosa

6

Fiona – A Clinical Psychologist, and a Commitment to Change

For sixteen years, I felt as though I was living in a long, dark, lonely tunnel. The darkness was my eating disorder, bulimia nervosa. This destructive relationship with food accompanied me through secondary school, grammar school, university and into my marriage and separation.

My relationship with food turned into a rope round my neck, dragging me down to depths unfathomable and deep, deep unhappiness. When I think of how I was then, I still shake my head and wonder how I could have lived like that. Yet I did, locked into a life I did not want to live but felt powerless to break out of.

My eating disorder crept up on me. My childhood could be described as 'average'. I didn't experience any particular traumas, although, like most people, I went through some unhappy experiences. My family were faced with eviction from our home when I was twelve. This caused a lot of arguments between my parents, which upset me. We moved from a friendly village to a town estate. During the year that followed, I had to face many changes – a new school; new friends to make; two well-loved uncles died, and the family cat also died. I felt I had to be 'strong', and not grieve. A year later, my best friend in the new estate ran away from home. I missed her tremendously, but her mother did not believe me when I said that I did not know where she was. My mother was working at this time, which caused more arguments between my parents, to the point that I thought they were going to get divorced.

I had felt slightly uncomfortable about my size and shape at primary school. I was less than five feet tall, and I loved food and eating, which was reflected in my rather rotund shape! At that age people rarely commented on my weight, so I did not worry too much about it. However, after failing my 'eleven plus' exam, I went to a secondary school where the boys were not so kind or tactful about my size.

After I came top of the class in the exams, the boys in the class reacted by teasing me about my shape. I only heard them call me 'Fiona fat gut' once, but the pain of hearing those words stayed with me for a long time. The irony was that the lad who had actually thought up the phrase was himself an unattractive, spotty boy who wore big glasses, so I could easily have hurled an insult back, but I was so taken aback that I said nothing in my defence, and just hurt inside.

This prompted me to go home and ask my mother if I could go on a diet; I was about thirteen at the time. I didn't give her any reason as to why I was concerned about my shape, and she tried to reassure me that I was not overweight, and told me not to be so silly. I therefore decided to take matters into my own hands, and I promptly stopped eating. I missed meals, telling my mother that I had already eaten at a friend's house, or had eaten too many sweets to want anything else.

After the 'Fiona fat gut' incident, I changed schools again. I went up to the grammar school for girls, where I was under pressure to achieve. Initially I managed to gain good results, which made me unpopular and I became more concerned about my shape, and continued missing meals. Weight began to drop off me. I think I was on the verge of becoming anorexic when my parents expressed their concern over me pushing some peas round a plate and trying to take the breadcrumbs off a fish finger. I have to admit that taking the breadcrumbs off a fish finger is a little obsessional!

I was torn between wanting to eat to please my parents, and wanting to avoid food because I was scared of putting on weight. Around this time I read a magazine article about someone who had an eating disorder. I thought, 'Gosh, that's the solution to my problem – I can eat and then make myself sick, to prevent me from gaining weight.' After that, when I felt upset or low, I would comfort myself by eating large quantities of food, and then I would make myself sick. By the age of fifteen, I was regularly binge-eating and then vomiting. I never imagined that the 'solution' to my desire to eat would develop into a nightmare and stay with me for years to come.

At the worst stage of my bulimia I would eat and then vomit from 7 am to 11 pm, taking breaks only to go out and buy more food so that I could continue bingeing. If I was alone, I could binge like this every day; at other times, I sometimes managed to binge just one day during the week. My whole life was taken up with thinking about food; it was my constant companion. Sometimes I planned what I would binge on the next day, but when the day arrived I would ignore my plans, and eat whatever was available. I often put frozen food in the microwave and ate it while it was only partly defrosted, or far too hot – I couldn't wait. I would eat anything and everything as long as I knew I could bring it up again.

My emotional state for the day would be conditioned by what I ate. If I managed to restrict myself and only eat fruit and cottage cheese I would feel fine. But if I so much as looked at a chocolate biscuit, I would tell myself off. If I ate it, I was the worst person to walk the earth – so weak that I couldn't resist a biscuit. I would feel so 'overpowered' that I would decide I might as well eat the whole packet, as I had already ruined the day.

Day in, day out I felt awful, both physically and emotionally. Physically, the binge–vomit cycle left me with a constant sore throat and dry mouth, while my stomach felt like the inside of a washing machine which was constantly on a spin and rinse cycle. Emotionally, I generally felt so low that life did not seem worth living.

My only escape from feeling terrible came during the early stages of a binge, when the world consisted of me and the food and the action of eating. It was as if time stood still. The binge would start off as a pleasurable release of tension, as I felt the food in my mouth, and the chewing and swallowing action. I was in a dream-like state, acting automatically. Then I would hit a mid-point stage where I suddenly 'woke up' and realised how much I had eaten. I would then feel that my stomach was so tight it hurt, and I would know that it was time to go off and be sick – making myself sick was physically painful. Often I would take a handful of laxatives as well, just to make sure that there was nothing left inside me.

After the cycle was over, I would sit on the floor, feeling worthless and unloved – how could anyone love a person who had such a disgusting habit? I would feel numb, and incapable of functioning. I would groan in pain, the pain being both physical and emotional. As soon as I could, I would break out of this 'zombie state', and put on a brave face – something that most people with bulimia are expert at doing. I would quickly wash my face, brush my teeth and put ice packs on my face to try and reduce the swelling. A bit of make-up would be the finishing touch, and then like the magician's assistant I could say, 'Hey presto', and in a flash of blue smoke be ready to face the world with a smile.

The smile hid deep unhappiness, tears and the emptiness of my life. It was more of an existence than a life. I put on the smile because I desperately wanted to hide the 'real me'. I was terrified that everyone would reject me if they knew what I was really like.

My eating disorder was at its peak during my late teens and early twenties. As I approached thirty, I tried to face up to the challenge of choosing the life I wanted to live, instead of spending vast amounts of time bingeing, vomiting and sitting on the toilet after taking laxatives. I was determined to get to grips with it, and my bingeing became less frequent.

On one level, I felt that I had everything I wanted. I had a job, my own house, a car, friends, and I had left a marriage in which I had felt desperately unhappy. The world was my oyster, and I had the chance to live life to the full. Except for one little hiccup. I still suffered from occasional binges, always followed by vomiting. My emotions would swing back and forth, between success at my achievements, and the depths of despair when once again I lost control of my eating behaviour. Glimmers of light had begun to penetrate my dark tunnel, but the sunlight was still a long way off.

So what was I going to do to get out of the darkness? I had been trying to get to grips with bulimia for a good five years, but even though I was a lot better than I had been, I was not able to kick the habit all by myself. I had not told anyone else about my eating problems, not even my closest friend. Perhaps I was too proud to own up to it, or too scared of what people might say. People perceived me as a confident, assertive, happy 'go getter'. Sometimes this was fairly true, yet inside there was a void which I tried to fill with food. Inside this secret place I hid all my messy bits, the parts of me which I found unacceptable. This included anger, insecurity, frustrations, guilt, sexual urges, lack of confidence and anything else which I wanted to avoid and hide.

Asking for help was one of the hardest hurdles I had to get over. Being self-sufficient and headstrong has its advantages, and facing up to not being able to recover by myself proved to be very difficult. I was extremely unhappy, and I realised that I was either going to continue living a life I hated, or I would need to give up some of my self-sufficiency and ask for help. Eventually, when I was twenty-eight, having had an eating disorder for almost half my life, I persuaded myself that looking for help could not be worse than carrying on this way. It was at least worth finding out what help was available.

The first step I took was to contact the national Eating Disorders Association (EDA); I had seen their address in a book. The EDA gave me the contact number for a local support group. I kept promising to attend, but every time the night of the meeting came round I would find something else to do. The something else would usually involve bingeing!

I had hoped that the information provided by the EDA would help me to convince myself that there were plenty of people who had much more severe eating disorders than I did, and that I had nothing to worry about. Instead of this, the information which I received persuaded me that my condition was serious, and that I should seek professional help. I plucked up the courage to go and see my doctor, on the pretence of another illness. As a parting statement I asked him if he knew of anyone who could help me overcome my eating disorder. I held my breath as I waited for his reaction, the seconds ticking by loudly in my head. Was he going to tell me to pull myself together, or to stop being silly and start eating properly? Or would he just look at me as if I had two heads and strike me off his list?

Contrary to my fears, his response was one of great concern and sympathy. He told me that he would refer me to a clinical psychologist for help, but it might take a few weeks before I received an appointment. I breathed a sigh of relief that at last I had found the courage to tell someone about my eating disorder, and he had not rejected me, but instead had offered to help.

This gave me enough courage to go along to the support group, where I had the opportunity to tell other people that I suffered from bulimia. When it was my turn to introduce myself, I wanted to be anywhere other than in that room. Just trying to get the words out of my mouth seemed to take so long. I wanted to rush out of the room, or at least bend the truth and say that I was there because 'someone I knew had an eating disorder'. But I took a deep breath, and let go of the secret which I had been holding close to me for so many years – 'I have bulimia'. Once I had said this, I again felt a great sense of relief. The pretence was coming down, and down for good. I didn't feel alone any more.

The group met every two weeks, and I attended, on and off, for about a year. I found it helpful to share my feelings and experiences with people who truly understood what I was speaking about. I was at last able to talk honestly and openly about my emotions, knowing that I would not be laughed at or ridiculed. I made one very close friend within the group, and we used to meet up and share exactly what was going on in our lives, without any embarrassment.

Some time after I had visited my doctor, the appointment to see the clinical psychologist arrived. I sat in the National Health Service waiting room thinking, 'I feel a fraud, what am I doing here, I'm not mad.' When Sally, the psychologist, came and asked me to go into the appointment room, I fully expected to be asked to 'lie on the couch'. The film industry has a lot to answer for! Thankfully the reality was very different, and we went into a very normal looking room, with two chairs. So began the process of exploring the way I was, how I thought and reacted to people, and why I used food in the way I did.

As well as helping me to understand myself and the way I was feeling, Sally offered practical help, using the 'bulimic programme'. This is a structured programme for people with bulimia, which recommends eating a specified amount of food at each meal, including sufficient carbohydrate. It has been found that eating binges are often triggered by not having eaten enough earlier in the day. When I ate sufficient carbohydrate, I no longer 'craved' food in the same way, and I was less likely to binge. While following this programme, I was asked to write down everything that I ate, and how I felt at the time. This was to help me identify whether there were particular situations or emotions which triggered my binge-eating episodes. I was also asked to record every time that I vomited or used laxatives.

Initially, I did not think I could manage to eat the amount of food specified by the programme. It involved eating more than I would usually allow myself outside of a binge. I was afraid that I would be unable to stop eating, and I was afraid that I would be unable to cope with having so much food inside me, and I was terrified that I would gain weight. Nevertheless, I was determined to try, as the rationale behind the programme seemed to make sense. It was at least worth giving it a go, as all my attempts to beat bulimia on my own had failed. This time I had the psychologist's support and encouragement, so I wasn't struggling on my own.

As well as feeling afraid, I also felt ashamed and embarrassed about the amount which I was eating. My view of what a normal portion was had become distorted, and I imagined that to follow the programme I would have to eat vast quantities of food. I hid my lunch in a drawer at work each day, so that no one would see that I had two whole rounds of sandwiches and consider me a glutton.

It took me a good three months before I began to get used to the set eating plan, and another three months before I could follow it comfortably. I realised that it was working, in that I was bingeing and vomiting less often, so I believed it was worth sticking to the programme. Although my meals were much bigger than before, my weight stabilised, and did not continue to rise.

As well as introducing me to the structured eating programme, the psychologist encouraged me to keep a personal diary, writing in detail about my feelings, hopes and worries. I found this diary very therapeutic. It was a safe place to release the emotions which were pent up inside me. Sometimes I showed Sally my diary, and sometimes I kept it to myself – the choice was left up to me.

One pattern which emerged from my diary was my difficulty in saying 'no' to requests which people made of me. If I did refuse, I would get very worked up and feel guilty about not helping. If I agreed to the request, I would feel resentful about agreeing to do something which I did not want to do. Often I would binge-eat, as a way of dealing with this resentment.

Part of the difficulty was that I couldn't bear to feel that anyone was angry with me, and for some reason I automatically linked saying 'no' with anger. Sally gave me opportunities to practice saying 'no' in our sessions, using role-plays. This helped me to overcome the fear that I felt in just saying the word, and I was encouraged to practise this in real situations as well. When I tried this, I discovered that, contrary to my expectation, most people did not get angry if I refused a request. Even if they did, I was able to explain why I was unavailable or didn't want to do what I had been asked to do. When I was able to say 'no' without feeling fearful and guilty, I felt released from the resentment which came with so often saying 'yes' grudgingly.

My appointments with Sally started on a weekly basis, but as I progressed they moved to being fortnightly, and then on to monthly sessions. After about seven months of following the bulimic programme I felt I had my eating under control. The binges were few and far between, and I felt on top of the world. I had made it – yippee! I agreed to stop seeing Sally, and I looked forward to getting on with my life.

I felt furious with myself when, about a month afterwards, the old habit began to trouble me again. It was so soon after treatment, and Sally had been so helpfu l– why was this happening? I had an occasional urge to eat a chocolate bar, and then I would want to make myself sick. I would get so nervous about having a date that I would binge and throw up before going out – which is not the best way to make you feel special before a date! Gradually the old pattern was resurfacing, not to the extent that it had done in years gone by, but still on a regular basis. I told myself, 'This is the way I am, part of me is always going to be bulimic, so I should just accept it and get on with my life.' This was a very low point in my life – I had known what it was like to be free of binges and concerns about food, and I had thrown it all away.

Feeling very discontented, I decided to go along to a day seminar about alternative therapies. I listened to some women eagerly discussing the new approach which one man had to offer. Their enthusiasm jarred with my low mood. I thought miserably, 'They're talking about him as if he was God! Nobody is that good.' I concluded that people put too much faith in other people, believing that they had the answers. For some reason, a new thought struck me, 'What is the whole point of my existence, what about God, where is God in my life?' My honest reply was, 'On the back burner with the gas switched off.'

Until I was twelve years old, I had been brought up to go to a village chapel. When we moved house I had stopped attending church. Since then I had ignored God because of my lifestyle, and because I felt I could not be of any value to him. Now I had been given a chance of full recovery from my eating disorder, and in my eyes I had sabotaged my own recovery. Why should I think that God would want such a mess of a person? I felt unworthy of love and forgiveness.

It was at this point that I heard about Anorexia and Bulimia Care (ABC), a Christian charity supporting people who suffered from eating disorders, and their families and friends. I was immediately struck by their logo, which claimed that 'There is an answer', and I wrote to them. I read through their literature, which stated that there is an answer to eating problems, through God who gives us unconditional love and sent Jesus to die for our sins so that we could have life in abundance. Initially I found these words a bit puzzling, but they also seemed challenging and encouraging.

I had reached a crossroads, an opportunity to move out of the darkness into the light. I seemed to have two voices fighting within me. One accepted the fact that I had decided to live my life as a bulimic, and argued, 'It's not so bad, I've lived with an eating disorder for a long time and it is familiar and comfortable. Lots of other people do it, so why shouldn't I?' The second voice challenged this by questioning, 'Why does food play such an important role in your life? It's not what God wants for you. To have life in abundance, you need to be free to have a loving relationship with God, not with food plus God.'

I wanted the love which God offered, although I found it very hard to believe that I could be loved. But I wasn't sure that I wanted to give up everything that came with my bulimia, even though bingeing made me unhappy. I felt that I was saying to God, 'Yes, I do want you in my life. But please leave me alone when I'm being bulimic; that's a part of me I don't want you to see'. Deep inside of me was a secret, and until I was willing to let God have control of even that part of my life, I was not free to fully accept all the love and wholeness which Jesus wanted to offer.

I began to read the Bible, and the truth started to sink in. God really did love me, where I was at that time, in the mess I was in. I realised that if God had created me and loved me, he must be sad that I was treating myself so badly. In order to move forward, I knew I would have to take certain steps, like saying sorry to God for the way I had treated myself, and trying to look after myself more lovingly. I needed to start nourishing myself both spiritually and with food.

I decided that it was time to renew my faith. I went to a Church of England service where I knew the vicar. My friend's parents attended that church, so I did not have to walk in on my own, which helped. It wasn't exactly to my taste, as I felt that the hymns were a bit slow, but on the whole the people were very welcoming. Passages in the Bible really came alive for me, which I found exciting. I had many fears at that time, and I found the Psalms especially comforting.

On Good Friday, I finally decided to give up being sick, and I made a commitment to myself and God that I was going to change for good. This meant going back on the bulimic programme, as I felt that was the way in which I could overcome the urge to binge. I had the option of going back to the psychologist and asking for support, but I decided against this because I didn't want to feel as if I was taking a step backwards. I wanted to avoid the shame of letting the psychologist know that I was not fully recovered.

Another possible option was to join the EDA telephone programme for bulimics. This involved following a similar programme to the one which I had used with Sally, but the support would be provided by regular telephone appointments, instead of at face-to-face sessions. I discussed this possibility with the local EDA volunteer, and she offered support and sent me a diary, so that I could follow the programme. In the end I decided that the diary was all I was willing to accept. Support had been offered, but I chose to 'go it alone'.

Like most people, I wanted to put off starting until 'tomorrow'. However, I had made a commitment, and I knew I should stick to it. So I started following the programme on my own, eating the suggested amounts as I had done under Sally's supervision. I managed to follow the suggestions much more easily than I had done the first time. Knowing I had succeeded once, however briefly, made the second time easier. It took me between three and six months to return to a sensible eating pattern.

During this second attempt at recovery, I turned to God in prayer. After eating the suggested amounts, I would pray that the urge to binge would go away. I also prayed for strength to manage the depression which I had suffered from, on and off, for many years. I went through the process of asking for forgiveness, and repenting of things which I had done wrong, and my resentment of other people. I was beginning to trust that God loved me.

As the days of normal eating became weeks, then months, then years, I gradually began to believe that I would not have a relapse. Occasionally the urge to binge would come back, and I would start thinking about food in ways which in the past had led to a binge. However, instead of automatically eating, as I had done in the past, I would sit and think about what had triggered this feeling – was it something I was anxious or upset about? I would identify the emotion (perhaps writing down my feelings), and then deal with it by talking to someone or praying, instead of trying to pacify my feelings with food. I have never binged or made myself sick since that Good Friday, six years ago, when I made a commitment to myself and God that I was going to change.

I have learned that independence is only one aspect of life. Although independence is good at times, we do not live purely as individuals. As Christians we belong to the body of Christ, the family of God, and we should be able to support each other. This doesn't mean that we have to bare all to every person we meet, telling them our life history. It does mean that we can experience friendship and companionship, and those who are struggling can receive help from others. I have learned to trust people, instead of being secretive and defensive as I once was. I am now able to receive love, and to love.

As I began to realise that God had brought me out of the dark tunnel into the light, and was offering me a life free from bulimia, I felt tremendous happiness – a happiness which I had never known before. It was liberating to find that food was no longer the first thing I thought of when I woke in the morning and the last thing I worried about as I fell asleep at night. I had at last been released to live life to the full, which is what God wants for us all.

Previously, I had believed that, in order to fully recover, I would have to identify the root cause of my eating disorder, and that after dealing with this, everything would fall into place. I had expected that there would have to be more talking, more digging through my life and trawling over past hurts, until the underlying cause finally came to the surface. This was somewhat depressing, as I had been trying to recover for years, and still hadn't managed to track down the cause. Each time I found one possible reason and started to consider it, another reason would pop up, and none seemed to be completely able to explain why I had developed bulimia.

Now, I discovered that it was not necessary to identify a cause for my eating disorder. I no longer needed to know, and I was able to stop the tiring search for explanations. I had peace of mind. I believe that God in his mercy chose to protect me from having to relive painful aspects of my life again and again. He gently freed me from their power.

Up until this point, I had been living in the world of 'if onlys'. If only my dad had shown more love, if only my mum had been more understanding, if only there was a magic pill to sort my eating out. I had many 'if onlys', but at the end of the day the only person who could do something about my bulimia was me. I needed to accept the things I could not change, and concentrate on the things I was able to do something about.

During times of prayer, I felt great burdens being lifted from me. Although I had hoped that after one prayer God would immediately sort out all the mess in my life, I found that he did not work like that in my case. Instead, I have experienced an ongoing process of healing and growth. Reading books, hearing sermons, attending conferences and retreats, and singing hymns have all at various times helped me in my journey towards greater wholeness. Listening to other people's experiences has helped me put my life into perspective.

As my recovery progressed, I began to get involved with helping other people. I offered support to people who suffered from eating disorders, by assisting with a support group and writing letters of friendship. I also got involved with other areas of voluntary work. Doing such work helped me value myself as a person whom God can use.

We all have gifts which are special to us and individually given by God. I believe that the relationship people with eating disorders have with food suppresses these gifts. I encourage people with eating disorders to do two things. Firstly, I recommend that they consider how they would like to live life without an eating disorder. Secondly, if they are physically well enough, I suggest that they go ahead, and use their gifts to gradually grow with the support and love of God.

I have changed in many ways during my years of recovery. One day I found the diaries I had written while I was bulimic and started to read them. They seemed so depressing and morbid, and so 'not me' anymore, that I burnt them. I had put that part of my life behind me, and burning the diaries was symbolic of this, a bit like a sacrifice. I had given that part of my life over to God, and all I wanted to remain were the ashes.

It is only through God that I have been able to change. Knowing that I am not alone, and that there is someone who will share my difficulties and sorrows, gives me hope for tomorrow.

I still enjoy using the gifts God has given me. I am currently a 'lay leader' with pastoral responsibilities at the church I attend. This is something I do as part of a leadership team, so that we can support each other. During the week, I work as an assistant health and safety advisor. My husband and I have a young son, who brings us a lot of joy. I'm learning every new day that I can trust in God, and give thanks to him for the greatest gift he has given me – which is life.

7

Amy – A Home of Healing

I had a lonely early adolescence. Both my parents were out most of the time with demanding full-time jobs, and I was left very much to myself. I was good academically, and very bookish, and I didn't bother much with friends outside school hours. The family rarely spent time together and I never felt that I had my parents' real approval. They sent me and my brother to Sunday school as children, but my father is an atheist and my mother an agnostic and fairly hostile to the church, and they never laid down a clear set of values and beliefs for us to follow.

It was difficult to ascertain exactly what would and what would not secure their approval. They were not demonstrative people, and rarely hugged or kissed, or showed affection in any physical way. Their own relationship probably contributed to this, as it was always very unstable and fraught. I grew up believing that demonstrations of affection or admissions of the need to be loved were signs of weakness. I never felt good enough, except in the academic field, where I obtained consistently high marks, accompanied by much praise from my teachers. I started to strive for perfection, hoping to gain my parents' approval that way, but I didn't receive it, or at least, not in a way that I could recognize and appreciate. Eventually I began judging myself by the same high standards. I could never try hard enough or be good enough.

The only area in which I did seem to be good enough was the control of my own body. I found that I could diet and lose weight very effectively. Food seemed to be a natural focus for exercises in self-control and for gaining my parents' approval. My mother had been on crash diets and exercise regimes ever since I could remember. Her see-sawing weight and her obsession with her shape were the determining factors in her self-image. I subconsciously picked up on her attitudes towards food, and concluded that being slim must be a way to gain happiness and approval, although I never articulated this at the time. I later learned that she had suffered from bulimia nervosa herself, which probably explains the violence of her reaction against me when I became first anorexic and then bulimic – a lot of her pain was caused by feelings of guilt.

By the time I was sixteen and had finished my O-levels (with a string of straight A grades which still didn't convince me that I could do anything 'well enough'), I weighed less than six stone. At this time, my parents had a very rocky relationship, and they were increasingly pulling in different directions over how I should be treated. The insecurity this caused me, along with the deep insecurity picked up subconsciously from my mother, was death to our relationship when things began to go wrong in my own life. When I first started losing a lot of weight, they tried to understand, and my mother took me to a doctor, who referred me to a counsellor. My parents were willing to do anything to help, taking me to see doctors, counsellors, psychiatrists and dieticians. But I wanted to feel that I was in control and when I felt that my parents were trying to control my eating habits, I found this an unbearable threat. I reacted with hysterical fear and outbursts of anger. They responded with their own anger, pain and fear, which led to huge, destructive rows. Some of the things we said and did to one another at that time took years to heal.

I continued to lose weight rapidly. Eventually I was admitted as an in-patient to an adolescent psychiatric unit, where I was put on bed-rest with a weight-gain diet for seven months. During this time I received a lot of counselling and therapy, including a few sessions of family therapy, which were disastrous. My brother refused to attend at all, and my father was not even prepared to consider that the family set-up might have contributed to my problems, and that changes might be needed if I was to be helped. My mother felt too personally threatened, hurt and guilty to continue being open to me in love. She froze up completely during therapy sessions. She put up her defences and strove to be an impartial, indifferent carer, not allowing me close enough to hurt her. At times, her studied indifference couldn't check the weight of emotion it was supposed to be holding back, and her feelings would burst out in the form of violent rage, and accusations that I was doing it all on purpose. My conviction that I was such a bad person that I had even alienated myself from my parents' love – which I had thought was the greatest love any person could have for another – caused me deep insecurity and self-hatred.

When I regained enough weight to be considered 'safe' (managing to maintain a weight of seven stone), I was discharged from hospital. I went on to study A-levels at sixth form college. The eating problem, however, had not been properly dealt with and was only just 'under control' throughout this period of time. I kept my weight artificially low for three years by weighing every item I ate and keeping a strict and precise record of the calories I consumed every day. My family had never gone in for communal meals – we all ate what we felt like, when we felt like it – so there was nothing to stop me going my own way, and feeling ever more out of control even as I strove to gain stricter control over my food intake.

After completing my A-levels, I went to university. I was still underweight and although I was nineteen, I had the body of the average thirteen year old. I had never had periods. My deprived body was craving more food, and this, combined with the complete anarchy of student eating habits, led me to begin to binge-eat. I was terrified of gaining weight, and so after bingeing I would make myself vomit. Within a few months I was bingeing and vomiting at least once a day, and often more than this. The binges grew bigger and bigger and the amount I was spending on food soared, quickly consuming all my savings. I was still seeing a counsellor, a doctor and a psychologist. I learned to define and understand the problem, and I spoke a lot about my relationships with my family and friends, but nothing could stop me when I felt the overpowering need to binge.

By the second year at university, my life revolved around huge binges every day, and constant cravings for food. I was filled with guilt and self-loathing because of my inability to live up to my own standards of perfection. I became deeply depressed. My doctor prescribed the anti-depressant Prozac, which didn't entirely remove the depression, but did lift the worst of the lethargy, so that I was at least able to get out of bed and try to go on, although I lacked any real 'oomph'.

Counselling provided a periodic release for pent-up feelings, and gave me a forum to discuss some of the fears which I didn't feel safe enough to mention elsewhere. Several of my friends who knew about the problem were also very supportive and caring. Some of them had problems with food themselves, although I didn't meet anyone else whose life was ruled by it quite so much as mine.

What was needed to break this destructive cycle was unconditional love. I'd always believed that my parents' love for me was unconditional, but in fact it wasn't. Their love was a general good-will towards me as long as I didn't 'go too far'. They would bend over backwards for me as long as they could still live by their own agenda, have their own lives, and attend to their own needs and wants. That is completely natural and the way we all live – there is no trace of blaming my parents in what I am saying. But the situation demanded more of them than they were able to give. The love they had for me was real in human terms, but it wasn't the love that lays down its life for another.

During my turbulent years at university, when bulimia got a stranglehold and I often felt despair, I started going to church. I met some mature and deeply-committed Christians who were willing to risk the potential pain of getting close to me. It was among these Christians that I found my most supportive friends. Their help, and the church services I attended, gradually convinced me intellectually of the truth of the gospel, although it didn't make the journey from head to heart immediately, and my problems remained firmly with me.

Unlike my parents, who tried to distance themselves from me in order to avoid getting hurt, my Christian friends opened up their homes, their hearts and their lives to me. They did so in the full knowledge of what they were doing. I told them about my difficulties before they 'took me on', and was amazed when they didn't turn a hair, and invited me in anyway. Whatever I did, they went on loving – their attitude towards me didn't change. Unlike my parents, they were able and willing to get close to me, although this made them vulnerable to being hurt. In retrospect, I know just how hard that was for them at times. One of them is now my husband, so I have heard his point of view! They had something to sustain them which my parents lacked; they knew that they were loved by God, and the love they showed to me was the love of Christ, not their own (limited) human love. I believe that it is only possible for human beings to sustain such love if they're backed up by something more than human. Discovering that I was loved unconditionally by God, and by other people who knew God, was the beginning of my recovery from my eating disorder. I began to dare to be normal.

By 'daring to be normal', I don't mean that I made a deliberate effort to eat regular meals and stop vomiting. That was the way I had always tried to tackle the problem before I began to recognise God's love. Past efforts to eat regularly had always resulted in failure, with me giving in to even bigger and more frequent episodes of binge-eating. For instance, one Sunday afternoon some time earlier, when I had felt tempted to binge, I had forced myself to go for a walk instead. As I walked around the park, I felt an ever-increasing sense of panic. By the time I got home, I had a severe headache and I felt as if I was going to burst with tension. I managed not to binge that day, but by the following day I felt that the craving to binge was too strong to resist. I gave in and had a binge which was massive, even by my standards. A typical binge for me might be a loaf of bread with butter and jam, six or seven bars of chocolate, a family pack of crisps, two or three packets of biscuits and perhaps a few doughnuts as well. A massive binge was – *massive*!

When I started 'daring to be normal', I started changing my attitudes and beliefs, rather than focusing on changing my eating patterns. The eating changed later as a result of the personality changes. I had hated myself for a long time, and I believed that people only cared for me either because they pitied me, or because they were stupid and couldn't see what I was really like – how deceitful, cowardly and selfish I was. I was challenged to think again when I began to realise, with a shock at first, that some people really did love me as I was, and were not simply pitying me or ignoring the truth. In particular, this was true of Sue (a church worker) and David (who became my husband). After my graduation from university, Sue invited me to live with her for three months, even though she knew about my problems and they remained severe all the time I lived with her. To friends like Sue and David, I was more than my bulimia. I discovered that I didn't have to be ill or needy to get their attention. I could just be me – *and they would still love me*! Other people had probably valued me before this, but this was the first time I *felt* valued as a person.

A year after I had lived with Sue, David persuaded me to spend a week at a Christian 'home of healing'. This was a Christian community where people who were ill or were seeking God's answers in their lives were invited to stay as guests for a week. During that time, they were able to attend services, and

117

be prayed with. There was someone available to talk with at all times, although they did not have to talk if they didn't want to. The idea was not to attempt extensive counselling, but to let God work.

That week was a real turning point for me. What happened to me during it enabled me to let go of the eating problem and give it to God. It is not easy to explain precisely what I mean by 'giving it to God' because it's something God enabled me to do, not something that can be done by following a set method. The pattern of my healing may be similar to that of many others, but God never deals with any two people in *exactly* the same way, because we all have different and unique needs, which only he fully understands.

When I arrived at the home of healing, I was feeling very low and nervous. I told Jane, the lady who was helping me there, that I felt I was a dreadful person. Usually when I said that sort of thing to anyone, they replied with affirming words such as, 'No, you're not awful at all. I think you're rather nice!' This would temporarily comfort me, but then I would think that the person affirming me didn't know how I felt or didn't know the real me. Jane's response was unexpected, and it shocked me. She replied briskly, 'Yes, you probably can be pretty awful. But God knows that, and he loves you anyway.' Suddenly, I felt I didn't have to hide any more. The awful 'me' I'd tried to conceal from other people was suddenly out in the open, and was still loved – not only by Jane, David and Sue, but by God.

The next step for me was to learn that God wanted to help me change. I had always thought that I had no control over bulimia. That had been proven by my attempts to control it by willpower, as I always ended up having a huge binge. I now discovered that rather than using my willpower to try not to binge, I needed to use it in a different way. I learned that I could use my will to choose to hand the problem over to God. This happened when I realised, during that week, that I needed God more than I needed the bulimia as a coping mechanism. On the Wednesday night I attended a church service, and at the end I went to the front in order to be prayed with. This was termed 'receiving ministry'. In that church, it was known that people often fell over, as if they had fainted, when they were prayed for. This was referred to as 'being slain in the Spirit', and I imagined that people had some kind of amazing spiritual experience when they fell over. I wanted to experience this too. When I went up to ask for prayer, I expected I would feel some kind of thunderbolt which would leave me healed and free and jumping for joy. I certainly expected something dramatic to happen. But, in my case, nothing seemed to happen at all. I didn't fall over, and the only thing I felt was a sense of rising panic. I couldn't bear it. I felt excluded and rejected and I ran out of the building.

I found a quiet spot in a nearby field and sat down in complete despair. It looked like God was healing everyone who asked him except me. I felt as if he didn't want me and couldn't heal me. But I also realized, as never before, that if I turned my back on God, I had nothing left at all. I had reached a point of no return.

I must have sat there for about an hour, and eventually I calmed down. I decided that whatever happened I was going to have to trust God, even if he wasn't apparently doing anything. I walked slowly back inside, and went to find Jane. I told her what had happened – or rather, what hadn't happened, and how I felt about it. Her reaction was, again, surprising. Instead of sympathizing with me, she asked me how I knew God wasn't doing anything. Had I given him a chance? I realised that I had gone to him with preconceived ideas of how I was going to feel, and what he was going to do for me. When he hadn't conformed to my expectations, I had flown into a rage, and demanded that he do what I wanted. I was expecting God to give me certain good feelings, but I was ignoring what he was saying to me.

When I had gone to the front of the church and the pastor had prayed with me, I had seen in my mind a picture of myself as a sheep which had fallen onto a rocky ledge halfway down a cliff. The sheep was making a lot of noise and panicking and struggling, but the shepherd didn't come. It was only later that I realized that I was like a sheep which was so busy thrashing about and making a noise, that I couldn't hear Jesus the Shepherd's voice above my own! I had to be willing to stop yelling and trying to rescue myself, and instead to admit to Jesus that I was stuck, and that I needed his help. I needed to relax, and to stop thinking about what I was going to do to help myself, and instead wait for him to act. Above all, I needed to stop asking God to do things my way, and allow him to do things his way. I was surprised by how hard that was for me – I hadn't realized how much pride was in the way.

I felt that God wanted me to let go of my bulimic habits, by acknowledging a number of things which I found it hard to admit. Firstly, I had to stop using my bulimia as an excuse for all my faults and selfish behaviour. Secondly, I had to confess that I had wanted healing only on my own terms. There were aspects of bulimia which I really enjoyed and did not want to give up – for example, the taste of the foods I ate during binges. A third realisation was that at this point, if I was honest, I actually preferred to have an eating disorder but still have control over my own life, rather than risk letting God have control. I needed to decide whether I really wanted to overcome the bulimia or not, if it meant losing my excuse for my behaviour, having to stop bingeing, and allowing God to be in charge of my life.

I felt very low on the day after the healing service. I spent a lot of the day in my room, struggling to take on board what I felt God was teaching me. I was faced with the truth that if I accepted the sort of healing which God was offering, it would *not* be all on my terms, and life would not be what I wanted it to be all the time. We do not have freedom to do exactly what

120

we want to. We are either 'slaves to sin' or 'slaves to God' (Romans 6:20–22). Being a slave of God means following his rules. Paradoxically, if we follow God's rules, we become truly free, because he made those rules in order to make us into the people he wants us to be. The result of my attempts to be totally free to do as I wished had been disastrous. I hadn't coped with complete freedom, and I had chosen bulimia as a way of surviving. A friend of mine once said, 'You're free to do as you like. But you're not free to stop doing it.' How very true. I wasn't capable of dealing with total freedom in my life, and that was because I wasn't designed to be. We are designed to find freedom through obeying God's rules. 'For best results, follow the manufacturer's instructions'.

At that point, I sensed God's presence. I know it must have been God, and not my imagination, because he was completely different from how I had imagined he would be. Loving, yes, but tough! Gentle, but totally uncompromising. I felt that he was saying, 'I offer you life: life on my terms. I won't force you to accept it. You can say "no". But if you do, you choose to turn your back on me, and I will not help you. I cannot help you unless you will let me.' I had the choice. God would not force me to accept him. I had to choose to take that step and say, 'Yes, I'll do it your way.'

The Friday and Saturday passed more quietly. I wasn't sure what had happened, but I had begun to see life in a radically different way. David, visiting on Saturday, was amazed by the change in me.

At the Sunday morning service before I went home, I saw a picture in my mind of a huge, deep-rooted poisonous plant being uprooted inside me. I asked for prayer again during the time of ministry at the end of the service. Again, I felt very small, and again I didn't fall over. I retreated to the toilets, feeling very tearful and wanting to run way. Then it occurred to me that God was still working, and that if I allowed a sense of resentment and injustice to rise in me because he had worked contrary to my expectations, I would be throwing his help back in his face – which was precisely what had been the problem all along! So I let go of the feelings of resentment and disappointment, and I felt a great sense of release, as I left the healing centre and went home.

A week after I returned home, I had a sudden, desperate desire to binge. I started to get a headache and to feel ill with tension. I ran to the front door in tears, set on buying some food to binge on. To my horror, David was standing on the doorstep. He was so upset by my frantic attempt to buy food, that he tried to hold me back by force. I went wild. I *had* to, I *must* binge! I'd *die* if I didn't! Suddenly, a voice in my head cut right through it all. 'How much of this is genuine and how much is acting?' it said. 'How much are you really out of control?' I silently asked God for help. I had a brief struggle with my pride. If I stopped yelling and screaming abruptly, would David think that the whole thing had been an act? I couldn't face him thinking that I was doing this for attention – I knew I wasn't. I realized that I was on the boundary between a state of severe anxiety which I couldn't prevent, and a state of hysterics which I could. At this point, I could choose not to cross the boundary. Once crossed, I would be unable to go back, and I would be compelled to binge. I chose to stop myself before I progressed even further into a state of anguish. The moment I took that decision, God stepped in, and gave me the strength to carry it out.

I stopped fighting and screaming and said to David in a normal voice, 'You're right. I don't have to do this'. Then I realized it was true. The compulsion had disappeared. I still felt anxious, but my anxiety was under control. The choice to 'let go' was mine, but the strength to do so (which only came after I had made the choice) was not mine. That's what I mean about willpower not being enough. I couldn't give myself the strength and motivation to carry through the choice I had made, but by making it, I opened the door for God's grace to come in and do the rest. God won't force himself in uninvited; I had to ask him to help. It was not easy for me to admit that I needed his help, but it worked, and it was worth it. I have yet to find a better way of dealing with such intense emotional situations, whatever they are about. I don't believe there is one.

The next step for me was to practise being honest with God. I used to think I was being honest when I prayed, 'Lord, help me! I don't want to binge!', but actually, I *did* want to! Part of me wanted to be thin at any cost, but also to eat the foods I craved. Honesty said, 'Lord, I do want to binge. I'm really tempted. But I know it's not good for me, so I choose to say "no" to myself, however painful that feels. And I trust you to honour that choice by giving me your strength to carry it out.' And he did.

That wasn't my last slip. I lapsed several times in the next six months. I binged, and then felt dreadful. But I realized that if I really repented and continued trying to 'let go and let God', I would be forgiven each time and could try again. Handing things over to God isn't a one-off process. Most of my Christian friends also say that they find themselves handing problems over to him, then grabbing them back, and later handing them over again. By the end of six months, my binge–vomit habit had tailed off and disappeared. I didn't even want to binge any more, a situation which I couldn't have imagined six months earlier.

As regards food, in the year after my visit to the home of healing, observing and copying David's eating habits helped a lot. He had known what it was to be hungry, and so he had a very pragmatic attitude to food. 'You eat what's on offer, you eat regular meals, you eat as much as you need, but no more, you eat if you're hungry, and don't if you're not.' I regulated my diet by eating the same as he did. Sometimes that meant eating slightly more than I would have allowed myself before, but I came to realise that by eating a bit more (the amount my body required in order to maintain a stable weight, in fact), I thought about food less. I didn't crave food, because my body was satisfied for the first time in years. During the first few months I did put on some weight, and then it levelled off and it has remained the same ever since, with no restrictions on what I eat. I feel healthier than ever before. I weigh ten stone, and look and feel fine. This weight is a bit higher than the weight I would ideally like to be, but it's obviously the weight my body likes to be. If I lose weight I start to feel ill and get attacks of hypoglycaemia. I don't bother weighing myself any more, and I use my clothes as a rough gauge of whether I'm putting on weight or losing it. I got rid of all my 'little girl' size clothes from the anorexia years. There's no point in fretting because I can no longer get into them – a normal woman *shouldn't* be able to get into them!

After a few months of regular eating, my body started to regulate itself. I no longer need to copy David's eating habits, because my body tells me what it needs. I have learned to listen to it, neither denying it, nor over-indulging it.

Nowadays, the anorexia and bulimia are entirely gone. I eat a healthy, balanced diet, and I don't think very much about it. I'm not obsessed with weight, healthy eating or dieting, although at times of insecurity I still sometimes like to be reassured that my body is OK. David is a great support in this, and is a constant source of affirmation for me. I'm still far too prone to see the negative side of things, and having a positive, optimistic husband around helps.

I go for longer and longer periods of time without attacks of depression and insecurity, and when they do come, they're less severe than they used to be. I know that it is OK to feel low, and that most people do from time to time, and that if we sit it out, things will improve. I no longer eat to cover up my feelings. I am able to trust people and talk to them when things are difficult. I'm slowly – very slowly – learning to have such confidence in the unconditional love of God and of other people, that I know that they won't reject me if I sometimes behave badly or get things wrong. In the past, I blamed myself for my illness, and felt that I deserved it because I was unlovable. Maybe that is one reason why I did not initially put much effort into trying to recover. Now, in contrast, I realise that although I do things wrong and make mistakes (as everyone does), God forgives me, and wants me to live life to the full anyway. As a result of having been through pain and problems, I have a better understanding of how other people feel when faced with emotional difficulties, and I have begun to develop a ministry of reaching out to others. I'm able to give love, as well as to receive it. I couldn't serve God while I was spending whole days forcing food into my mouth and then bringing it back up again. Now, however, I am able to make a serious attempt at living for God.

David and I have been married for three years, and we do not yet have children. At first I was terrified of having a child of my own. I felt that my mother had contributed to many problems in my life – sometimes in ways which were outside her control. I thought that I would be bound to fail my own child too. Mothers have so much power and influence, even in areas where they don't want it. Now that those things are further in the past, I can look more objectively, and see that I don't need to repeat my mother's mistakes. I have God to help me, and she didn't. I have a more supportive husband and many close friends. Because of my own experience, I am aware of many of the potential pitfalls. I won't be a perfect mother – not by a long chalk – but I don't have to be. Perhaps by trying to be perfect, we make more of a mess of things than if we accept our imperfections, hand them over to God, and get on with it. David and I can't afford to have children at the moment, and I don't feel ready yet, but we're both quite definite about wanting to have them in the future. The body can take several years to recover from the abuse it receives through anorexia and bulimia. For example, my menstrual cycle is still not completely regular, although my weight has been stable for more than four years. Hopefully in a few years time I will be able to bear a healthy child.

I have learned many lessons through my own difficulties. One is that healing does not necessarily happen all at once. I stopped bingeing and purging within about a six-month period, which was very swift given that I had suffered from eating disorders for eight years. But my eating disorder was only a symptom of much deeper pain. Once the symptom had been dealt with, God started to work on the deeper hurts. My recovery from the underlying causes was not so rapid. If God had sorted out all the problems in my life instantly, it would probably have killed me! I see it as comparable to having major surgery. A surgeon won't just plunge in the knife and cut everything out at once. Infection has to be removed slowly and carefully, bit by bit, giving the patient time to recover between each new shock to the system. God is the master surgeon, and he knows what he's doing. My healing has taken years and will go on for the rest of my life. Recovery is partly a learning and growing process, where hurts need to be worked through and prayed about in an atmosphere of unconditional love. An instant cure would not allow me to grow as a person and as a Christian. God doesn't want to make me into a perfect robot, he wants my co-operation in the process of forming me.

Although I could not recover simply by using my own willpower, God has allowed me to play a part in my own healing. I had to *decide* to let go of my eating disorder, and of my fears and pains, and hand them over to God. He only started to deal with them after I handed them to him – because he has given us free will, and will not push his way into our lives uninvited. Letting go has been difficult and painful, but it has been worth it. I have learned that healing does not always happen in the way or at the speed which we want. God has said, 'My thoughts are not your thoughts, neither are your ways my ways' (Isaiah 55:8). I have chosen to trust God to heal me in his way and in his time, even when I don't understand what he's doing.

I trust that he knows better than I do.

Another important lesson for me has been learning that the only way to true healing is through complete honesty with God and with yourself. I found it frightening and extremely painful to face up to some of the things I had done, but I discovered the reality of Jesus' words that 'the truth will set you free' (John 8:32). By facing the truth head on, I was able to be freed from feelings of guilt, fear and insecurity about the stranger hidden inside myself. I found that, incredibly, however awful I may think I am, God still loves me. Being afraid of who we are won't change the truth. Only by facing it honestly and letting God change us can we be set free. One of the things that strikes me when I meet a really holy person is their transparency: they literally have nothing to hide. They have no need to fear what would happen 'if anyone found out about such-and-such', because they have already faced it and brought it out into the open before God, and it has lost the power to hurt them any more.

The third major lesson which I learned was that I need God. I have a lot of gifts and talents and it is all too easy for me to fall into using them instead of relying on God. When things are going well, I can be tempted to think that I can get on OK by myself. At such times, the depression and hurts lingering from the anorexia and bulimia years are like St Paul's 'thorn in the flesh' (2 Corinthians 12:7). They raise their ugly heads every so often to remind me that it's not me who is doing the good work, it's God in me. Only by keeping in fellowship with God and his church can I go on growing. At times of depression, I often can't feel God's presence at all, and that's when I know how much I really do need him. At those times, it's important to ask others to pray for me. Then I can be sure that God is working in me still, in response to their prayers, even though I don't feel able to pray myself.

I am learning how to support other people who are suffering from eating disorders. From my own experience, I know the importance of showing people with eating disorders that they are loved. Many of them feel guilty, have low self-esteem and hate themselves, just as I did. Any reaction towards them which could be interpreted as rejection, will be. If they fear rejection, they won't dare to be honest, which makes it very difficult to help them. I know that my own strength is not always enough when I am trying to support other people, as I can be left feeling drained and hurt. The person with the eating disorder will then feel even more guilty and rejected. I need to work in God's strength, and it's also useful to have friends around me who support me in what I'm doing, and pray for me. This must be even more essential for people who actually live with someone who has an eating disorder. Recovery is a slow and often excruciating process, and the need for God's strength and the support of fellow Christians is acute.

It can be useful to recommend that a doctor, counsellor or psychologist is involved. When it is necessary for someone to 'play the heavy' and force the individual to eat, or stop eating, or to face certain issues, that role should be left to a professional. Those who have a personal relationship with the person with the eating disorder should not have to take on this role.

Many people with eating disorders, if they are honest, are not sure whether they want to get well. Getting well involves change, and change can be a frightening prospect. Most people do not need to go to a home of healing in order to come to the point at which they are ready to change. What happened to me at the home of healing could happen in any loving Christian home. It is God who helps us change, not necessarily specific places or people. If someone with an eating disorder can be provided with a loving and safe environment in which they can have the confidence to allow God to work in them, they may feel secure enough to risk stepping forward in the recovery process.

That has been my own experience, and my prayer is that many other people with eating disorders will also reach that place of healing.

8

Stephanie – Healing of Memories

Half a grapefruit and a diet yoghurt for breakfast; diet soup for lunch, and two crispbreads with cottage cheese and salad in the evening. That was my daily diet when I was twenty-one. I was suffering from anorexia nervosa. I stopped menstruating as my body tried to survive on the monotonous starvation diet. I did not receive any medical help at that point.

After a year of self-starvation, I gave in to my craving for food and I started to binge-eat. I was still afraid of gaining weight, so I would purge after bingeing. At this stage, I decided to seek help from my doctor for the depression which accompanied my eating problems. Just as I had moved from not eating to bingeing, so too I moved from receiving no help to receiving a surplus of help. I started seeing a psychiatrist, who 'happened' to attend the same church as I did. I also had sessions with a psychotherapist at a local hospital, and I met with my own pastor. In addition, I studied a lot of counselling and self-help books. I found this 'binge' of help very confusing, as I received a lot of contradictory messages.

I reached the stage where I realised that, despite all the help, little was changing. I cried out to God to change me, as I was desperate for healing. I had read testimonies of people who had been healed instantly, when God had touched and transformed their lives and I wanted that to happen to me. At that time, God showed me, in my mind, a picture of an oil painting. It was beautiful, but someone had painted a horrible picture over the top of it. The original artist was carefully removing the top painting, and here and there glimpses of the beautiful picture below were shining through. The artist was working slowly because to rush the job would the risk damaging the original.

As I prayed about this experience, I believed that God wanted to teach me that I was like the beautiful oil painting underneath. He wanted to remove the mess that was covering my life, and to let the beauty shine through, but he wanted to do it slowly, like the master artist, so that I could emerge complete and undamaged. He was taking a long time to restore me, not because he didn't care, but because he did. I knew that God was working in my life according to his plan and timescale, not mine, and I was able to trust that his way was best. This had the effect of producing patience and endurance in me.

My recovery was a long, convoluted journey. Sometimes I felt that I had taken one step forward and two steps back, but the important thing was to keep moving towards recovery. When I go for journeys in my car, I often don't go straight where I'm aiming for, because I have an awful sense of direction. This does not stop me trying to go places. I just have to stop and think and look at maps, and try to understand where I went wrong so that I don't make the same mistake again. My journey of recovery was rather like that, sometimes taking a roundabout route, but helping me move on nevertheless.

One of my circuitous journeys came when I was about halfway through my recovery. While I was very ill, I made a vow to God that if I got better, I would stop weighing myself. As I progressed, I tried to stick to this vow. However, I had a relapse, and became concerned with my weight again. I joined a slimming club, where I was weighed. On my first evening at the club I challenged God, thinking, 'This is where I belong God – what are you going to do about it?' The next week when I went along, I was informed that I had been 'thrown out' of the club! The application form which I had completed had asked the question, 'Have you ever had an eating disorder?', to which I had replied in the affirmative. The lady who ran the group explained that they did not accept people who had suffered from eating disorders. I felt rejected, embarrassed and hurt, and yet I knew that I had brought this on myself by breaking my vow. God was bigger than I was!

I found it helpful to keep a daily diary. On days when I felt I had failed, it was encouraging to look back and see the progress I had made, which could easily have gone unnoticed. I wrote down my feelings about the things which happened each day, and how I handled (or failed to handle) my emotions. I realised that God was slowly changing me.

I tried to do things which would get me away from thinking about my own problems, and help me think about other things. It was all too easy to keep falling into a pit of self-centredness, with my needs and problems becoming all-consuming. Although it was important for me to face up to what was happening in my own life, rather than deny that there were difficulties, I also found it helpful to take time to think about other people, and to do things for them. I started to visit a residential home for elderly people, with my dog Angus, who was a registered PAT dog (Pro-Active-Therapy). Just seeing other people, talking with them and meeting their needs for friendship and a listening ear gave me a new perspective on my difficulties. I knew that other people found it tiresome if I only spoke about my problems, and so I tried to have other interests to speak about as well.

God moved gradually and gently in my life, healing areas of hurt and brokenness, and bringing restoration. Then, on one miserable summer day, when it was pouring with rain, I experienced what I believe was the turning point in my recovery. I had felt that God had something he wanted to say to me that day, but I had wanted to run away instead of listening to him, as it seemed easier. Late in the day, unable to escape his 'nagging', I knelt by the side of my bed and was still, finally willing to listen to him. As I knelt there, God revealed to me three scenes from my life, one after the other.

The first was when I was five years old. My mother used to be a 'dinner lady' in my school, dishing up the school lunches. I disliked the school meals, and I rarely ate much. On the particular occasion which God reminded me of, I was told that I had to eat the food. To make matters worse, one of the boys who sat at my table worried me, by saying that he was on a hunger strike because the food was awful. I was afraid that he would starve to death.

The next scene was when at about the age of ten, I stayed with my aunt for a few days while my mother helped my sister look after her new baby. I was a finicky eater, and my aunt told me that all the starving children in India would be glad of the nice meal which I had not done justice to. I felt very upset about this.

The third memory was the most painful one. My father had a nervous breakdown when I was eleven, possibly due to being over-prescribed medication. The scene which came to mind was the day when mum, dad and I were seated round a table, about to eat lunch. We each had a glass in front of us, and dad stood up to pour a drink from a jug into the glasses. What he didn't realise was that the glasses were upside down. The drink spilt everywhere. My mother shouted loudly at him, and I sat very still, wanting to leave the room but feeling too frightened to do so. When I re-lived this scene in my mind, I sobbed for a long time.

As my crying subsided, God brought the three scenes back into my mind, but with a difference. He showed me that he was with me at each of these painful times in my life. I saw myself at the school dinner table, but this time I saw Jesus sitting next to me. He watched me looking sadly at the plate in front of me, and said, 'Don't worry, I'll eat that for you.' I then asked him about my friend who was on 'hunger strike'. Jesus assured me that he would look after my friend, and that I didn't need to worry.

Next we were at my aunt's house. This time Jesus was standing at the side of the room. My aunt began her spiel about starving children, and I didn't know what to say. But I felt that Jesus was giving me the words, 'Don't worry, auntie. Whether or not I eat my dinner won't make any difference to them, but this afternoon we can go and pay some money to Oxfam for them to have food.'

In the final and most painful recollection, I could not see Jesus in the room with us, but I could feel his presence, like a radiance coming from one corner of the room. Nothing was said this time, but as dad spilt the drink, instead of mum shouting, we all laughed together about what had happened. When God showed me this, I laughed and laughed by the side of my bed.

Before this point, I had always been very sceptical about the 'healing of memories' – a phrase some Christians use when they speak about God bringing healing to painful personal experiences in the past. I had never read any books on the topic or thought much about it, nor had I thought about these three memories in my own past, or realised how significant they were in contributing to the fears I had around food. However, after God brought these memories back to my mind, I realised that I had been anxious about eating since I was very young, and I believed that these three examples of unhappy mealtimes had, to a large extent, caused this anxiety. Because of the negative associations of mealtimes in my past, I hated eating with other people, and I always ate furtively, on my own.

The immediate effect of seeing Jesus with me in these scenes, was that I felt free to see food in its right context. Suddenly I felt that mealtimes with other people could be enjoyable (just as we had laughed when re-visiting the scene where my father had spilt the drink).

When I was set free from my anxiety concerning food, I recovered fairly quickly from my eating problems. This was remarkable, as I had struggled with anorexia and bulimia for seven years. Some books by Dr Neil Anderson helped me as I became free from destructive ways of thinking. Dr Anderson writes from a wealth of experience in counselling people and seeing them released to know the wholeness which God intends for them. His book *Victory over the Darkness* contains scriptural teaching about who we are as believers in Christ. I found it useful to remind myself of my identity in Christ, and this liberated me to see myself as God sees me, instead of as a problem-ridden, no-hoper.

As part of the process of being set free, I decided to get rid of the clothes which were too small for me. In the past I had stood in front of my wardrobe and screamed because none of my nice, expensive clothes fitted me anymore. This had led me to binge-eat because I was feeling so bad, and then to punish myself afterwards. Having a wardrobe full of clothes which didn't fit put a terrible pressure on me to try to lose weight. Some of the clothes which I *could* get into were a tight squeeze and felt very uncomfortable. It was hard to get rid of clothes which I had spent a lot of money on and really liked, but it removed the pressure to fit into clothes which were too small. Most of the clothes I own now are from charity shops. They are good quality, the right size and feel comfortable.

I resolved to try not to evaluate myself by how many pounds I weighed. I now realise that there is no 'perfect weight' at which negative feelings stop; rather, when the underlying issues which cause an eating disorder are dealt with, weight loses its significance. Consequently, I rarely bother to weigh myself any more, although I know that I weigh around eleven stone. I am 5 foot 6 inches tall, and my size 14 clothes fit comfortably. When I was receiving help from my doctor, he set me a target weight of ten and a half stone. However, my body size and shape feel right and comfortable as they are. I think that it is better to be slightly 'overweight' and feel free to eat normally without worrying about food or weight, than to conform to weight and height charts and be obsessive about eating. I do not intend to diet for the sake of a few pounds. In any case, we all have different frame sizes, and we would not all necessarily look right at the standard weight for our height.

Mealtimes are no longer a problem for me. Two years ago I commenced Bible college. In the college, I eat with eighty other people, and I take my turn serving food, which is something I would have dreaded a few years ago. I am no longer obsessive about what I eat or don't eat. I am much happier now than I was previously, and I have learned to cope appropriately with my emotions.

God has not often shown me pictures like those I have described here. It has been a rare occurrence, and not something which I have looked for. But God did give me one more picture shortly after my relationship with my boyfriend broke up. We had planned to get married, and I had bought a beautiful wedding dress. People kept telling me that I should get rid of it, but I wanted to hang on to it 'just in case'. After I eventually removed it from my wardrobe, I saw a picture of myself standing at the front of a very picturesque old church, wearing a wedding dress. Sunlight was streaming through the stained-glass windows, onto the dress. As I turned round, I saw the back door opening, and I knew that Jesus was going to enter and walk down the aisle. I told a friend about this picture, and she said that I had got my facts wrong, because the bridegroom always waits for the bride at weddings, and not the other way round. However, after thinking about this, I realised that as Christians we are 'the Bride of Christ', and we wait for Jesus, the bridegroom – not the other way round.

I am now a voluntary 'befriender' for the Christian organisation, Anorexia and Bulimia Care. Having suffered from eating disorders myself means that I have a special affinity with those whom I befriend. I can offer real empathy, rather than just sympathy. While I was ill myself, the one thing I really wanted was to meet someone who had been through what I was going through, and had recovered, and was leading a normal life. My best friend arranged for me to meet someone at her church who had 'recovered', but unfortunately when we met up, she told me that she still had 'bad days' with bulimia. This led me to believe that nobody could really get over this illness; it seemed like a hopeless situation which I would simply have to live with. Now I have discovered that lasting recovery is possible. I have got over the eating disorder completely, thanks to God. That is why I want to share my story with other people who suffer from eating disorders. I want to encourage them to pursue healing and wholeness, and not to give up.

When I meet other people with eating disorders, I am careful not to imagine that their experience is exactly the same as mine. I know that every individual is unique, and God works in different ways in each person's life. I might think that someone needs help in the area of, say, self-esteem, whereas God might actually want them to deal first with the area of forgiveness. So, when I try to help someone, I pray for wisdom about what to say, rather than assuming that I know what is best.

Although God healed me by showing me pictures, I don't expect him to deal with everyone else in the same way. My own experience of inner healing happened by God's sovereign dealing in my life, not because I was trying to search for problems in my past and to resolve them. For people who are seeking healing for anything in their past which they think is hindering them, I would recommend that they speak with an experienced, qualified counsellor whom they feel they can relate to. It is important that people receive the right type of help. When I was seeing a psychotherapist, she advised me to do some things which went contrary to my Christian beliefs, although she knew that my faith meant a lot to me. As I was very vulnerable at that time, I followed her advice, and then struggled with a tremendous burden of guilt afterwards. It is important to choose people you can trust when you are seeking help, and not to do things which go against God's way.

I have learned not to underestimate the power of prayer. Prayer is the one thing which kept my mother sane throughout my years of difficulties, and it gave her hope that God would break into the destructiveness of my life. I asked several people to pray for me, but it was important that I also prayed myself, and was honest with God about how I was feeling. Even when I felt that my prayers were just 'hitting the ceiling', I kept praying. Prayer is not about changing God, but it can change us. I truly believe that God has answered the prayers which I offered, and has brought me through to a place of wholeness and peace.

Recovery from Anorexia Nervosa

9

Penny – Christian Counselling

I spent fourteen years in the wilderness of anorexia, stumbling along in the dark from day to day, dreading each new dawn and relieved at each day's end. The time seemed wasted. Why was I here? What was I doing with my life? As I look back now I can see that during this time God was with me, training me for the future. I can honestly say I have seen God's gentle, caring hand in my deliverance:

> I waited patiently for the LORD;
>   he turned to me and heard my cry.
> He lifted me out of the slimy pit,
>   out of the mud and mire;
> he set my feet on a rock
>   and gave me a firm place to stand.
> He put a new song in my mouth,
>   a hymn of praise to our God.
>   (Psalm 40:1–3)

When I was born in 1942, my father was away at war. My family consisted of my mother, my sister and myself. When I was two and a half, my father returned. I didn't know who he was, but I knew that he came between my mother and myself. From the time he came home, I became a difficult child. I wouldn't dress myself in the morning, because I always wanted my mother to dress me. At times I refused to eat my breakfast. One morning my father told me that I could not go to school unless I ate breakfast. I liked school very much, but on this occasion I picked up the toast and threw it at him! I was not allowed to go to school that day, and I can remember spending the day in my room crying and really hating myself. I think I disliked myself from that time on, and this contributed to my later troubles.

When I grew older I moved to a boarding school. I found it difficult to make friends there, and I was often on my own; I felt sad a lot of the time.

I found school meals especially stressful. The usual procedure was to allocate every pupil to a particular table for one week, moving round the table one place every day. A member of staff sat at one end and a prefect at the other end. When it came to our turn to sit next to the member of staff, it was our duty to keep up a conversation throughout the meal. We were told off if we didn't. Some staff members were difficult to talk to and so this could feel quite threatening.

On some weeks we were not allocated a table but had to 'fill up'. This meant waiting at the end of the dining room until grace had been said, then going round the tables asking if you could take an empty place. I and some other girls hated the weeks of 'filling up' and would sometimes hide at mealtimes to get out of it, which meant missing the meal. I think my hatred of mealtimes, and my delight when I successfully missed a meal, may have contributed to my developing anorexia, although this was not the main cause of my difficulties.

Because I was not happy at school, I left as soon as I could, just after taking my O-levels when I was sixteen. I then lived at home for a year, taking some more O-levels. Although I was glad to have left school, I was not happy at home either. I expressed my unhappiness by restricting what I ate. I grew obsessed with food and each day the amount I would allow myself became smaller and smaller. If I did eat anything extra, panic set in and I would subsequently eat nothing.

After about six months, when my weight had gone down to

five and a half stone, I was diagnosed as suffering from anorexia nervosa. I started to see a psychiatrist in Harley Street in London. I saw him every week, and he told my parents not to force me to eat. After another six months my weight had dropped even further, to just four and a half stone, and I had to be hospitalised. I was then seventeen.

I was admitted to a psychiatric ward, where I was forced to eat big meals. This did not work very well, and so I was put on bedrest, but I still did not gain much weight. After a year of making little progress, I was moved to the Maudsley Hospital, and was admitted to a metabolic ward specialising in anorexia.

At the Maudsley, instead of being given meals, I was put on a very high-calorie liquid diet. Every day I was faced with the dreaded bottle of liquid. It tasted awful and made me feel bloated and sick, but I had to finish every last drop by the end of the day. There was no opportunity to surreptitiously dispose of any, as my sink was covered and padlocked and a nurse was with me at all times. Although there were times when the liquid made me physically sick, I never intentionally made myself sick; it would have been pointless because when I was sick the dietician calculated the calories lost and gave me an additional drink to make up for them.

There were two good things about the drink. It was so awful that it bore no resemblance to food, which pleased me as I loathed food. In addition, it made me gain weight very rapidly. I had mixed feelings about this, hating the weight gain, but also wanting to get it over with so that I could leave the hospital.

The liquid diet did not deal with the real problem, or help when I had to tackle ordinary meals again. When I stopped taking the high-calorie drinks, the pattern of weight loss gradually repeated itself, until I was back to square one.

Eventually I managed to gain enough weight to be discharged. When I first left hospital I lost weight again and had to be readmitted. After I was discharged for a second time, however, I managed to survive on my own, albeit at a very low weight. I succeeded in holding down a job, but I stumbled from day to day in a miserable existence.

I had always thought that I was a Christian. I went to church regularly, and outwardly it looked like I lived a model life. Sometime after I had been discharged from hospital I met someone who explained what being a Christian meant and I suddenly realised that I was not really a Christian – that is, Christ was not at the centre of my life. I had never fully understood that Jesus Christ had died for me, and that I could confess my sins and come to God through him. That night I prayed, saying that I wanted to accept Jesus into my life, and to live as one of his followers. There was no dramatic change, but I started to pray regularly. Also I had some good friends who were concerned for me and we studied the Bible together.

Although I had become a Christian, I still detested myself. I was convinced that I was not worthy of either food or other things which give most people pleasure. I found it difficult to buy anything for myself, even a pair of tights, as I felt guilty if I spent money on myself. I was still an outpatient at the hospital and attended weekly sessions with the psychiatrist. On many occasions my Christian friends advised me to also see a Christian counsellor. They told me that only God had the answer to guilt. Looking back, I believe that this was helpful advice. I see that at the heart of many problems is a desire to control our own lives and a fear of handing our lives over to God. But at the time I did not see any reason why I should speak with a Christian counsellor, and I ignored the advice. I thought I was getting on all right and I wanted to do it my way.

It was only much later that I discovered that handing control over to God is the door to healing. I well remember the day this happened, a Saturday afternoon, when I was at the end of myself. I could no longer pretend that my way was working – it was obvious even to me that I was very ill with anorexia, and not enjoying life at all. My life was a big struggle and I felt unable to do anything about it. It was as if I were in a pit and there was absolutely no way out.

I knelt on the kitchen floor, in floods of tears, and said, 'Lord, just take my life and do whatever you want with it.' It was a desperate last resort, although really it should have been a first resort. I certainly meant every word.

That weekend I had been reading a book on depression called *A Mind at Ease,* written by Marion Ashton, a Christian doctor. I could identify very closely with the words. Later on the Saturday evening I told a friend that I thought I should follow her recommendation and see a Christian counsellor. In this way, I was admitting that I was not managing on my own. To my astonishment she said that the person she wanted me to see was the author of that book. With deep conviction I felt that this was God's loving way of encouraging me along his path. He was in control.

I met with Marion Ashton on a fortnightly basis at first, and then less frequently. She is a Christian who had some emotional difficulties herself in the past, and felt that God had called her to help other people with psychological problems. When I first walked into her room, I noticed that the Bible was open on her desk. It did not take me long to realise why. She approached problems in the light of the Bible. Prior to this, I had received a lot of counselling from various psychiatrists, and it had always been formal and clinical. The sessions with Marion, in sharp contrast, were informal and were based on my relationship with God, not on my efforts to change my behaviour.

Marion helped me to see how I viewed my life – as worthless and ready for the rubbish tip. She then revealed how God viewed my life, showing me that he says, 'You are precious and honoured in my sight, and . . . I love you' (Isaiah 43:4). She explained that my belief that I was useless was a lie of Satan, and I had to replace my view with God's view, as God's view is always the true one. It was a revelation to me to think that the devil had such control over my life. My belief that I was worthless had dominated my whole life. It had limited what I could do for God, and robbed me of my joy. In fact, it had nearly robbed me of my life.

Marion often quoted the Bible to help me see the truth, and she encouraged me to read and use the Bible in my fight against Satan. God's word is described as 'sharper than any double-edged sword' (Hebrews 4:12) and Marion explained to me that a sword is of little use unless it is used; likewise, the Bible must be picked up and used if it is to have any result. She helped me to distinguish God's truth from the devil's lies. I learned to fight against the lies which were in my mind, instead of simply accepting them, as I had always done. I started to reject them and replace them with the words of truth which are contained in the Bible.

I can remember standing at the photocopier at work, ploughing my way through a pile of documents to be copied, and repeating the words of Isaiah 43:4. It was all parrot fashion at first, churning out the same words again and again, just as the photocopier was churning out the same document time after time. I had for a long time known in my head that God loved me. As I repeated the words of truth over and over again, I came in time to accept them in my heart. This changed the way I felt about myself and consequently the way I behaved. I started to live in a way which demonstrated that I believed that I was precious.

I gained much encouragement as I continued to read God's word. I was struck by verses which likened me to clay in God's hands, reminding me that he is the Potter and I must be willing for him to shape me as he chooses (Isaiah 64:8). Often I read that with God I did not have to be afraid. This reassured me.

Soon after I started seeing Marion, I read another of God's promises, and felt that he was speaking directly to me. The words were: 'I will lead the blind by ways they have not known, along unfamiliar paths I will guide them; I will turn the dark-

ness into light before them and make the rough places smooth'
(Isaiah 42:16). Yes, my life was dark and there were many
rough places, but I knew for the first time, with an indescribable assurance, that God would heal me. It was a huge encouragement, something to hang onto and keep me going through
the long months of my battle.

Weeks went by, and although I was beginning to accept
myself as a worthwhile person, there was still no sign of being
able to eat more normally. I was shocked recently when someone reminded me how little I ate at that point — I had forgotten just how extreme I had been. I rarely ate breakfast, and
when I did it was just a small piece of toast. I often went without lunch as well, although sometimes I had a biscuit. In the
evening I allowed myself a salad or cold cooked cabbage. Going
to bed was the best time, as for some reason I felt safer then,
and I treated myself to a milky drink and a large piece of bread
and butter. At that time I weighed between six and six and a
half stone. I am 5 foot 4 inches tall, so I was extremely underweight.

I found it hard to eat with other people. I tried to avoid this
if at all possible, or else just to have a cup of black coffee. One
day I was having a meal (or, to be more accurate, my statutory
cup of coffee) with some friends and one of them said to me,
'Penny it's so nice to have you with us.' How much that simple statement meant to me. If they accepted me just as I was,
why shouldn't I?

I still felt inadequate and different from other people, and I
struggled to eat the minimum I needed in order to keep going.
I was trying to cope with a job and a normal life at a very low
weight. I had to believe God's promises even though I didn't
always feel his love or presence. It was like stumbling on blind-
ly, believing what I couldn't see.

There came a point when I was challenged by the fact that
I was telling my friends that God was going to heal me, but I
wasn't doing anything to help myself. I wasn't *trying* to eat nor-

mally. My counsellor likened me to a person about to undergo an operation to remove a growth. It would be foolish to say to the anaesthetist, 'Please don't sedate me completely, I want to help the surgeon with this operation'. We have to be willing to put ourselves completely into the hands of the surgeon and let him do the work. So it was with me. I had to put myself completely into God's hands and let him work in me.

About a year after I started to meet with Marion, God gave me another promise: 'Forget the former things; do not dwell on the past. See, I am doing a new thing! Now it springs up; do you not perceive it? I am making a way in the desert and streams in the wasteland' (Isaiah 43:18–19). I knew that God was doing something new in my life, and this encouraged me to keep going.

I knew I had changed when I began to buy ordinary things for myself. I started doing this on my own initiative. Previously, I had felt so trapped by guilt that I couldn't buy anything for myself. After I broke through this trap, and started to spend money on myself, it felt as if I had been set free. I was able to shop with joy and satisfaction. One day I bought a new pair of shoes, with great delight. I could not have dreamt of doing that a year earlier, because I felt I was not worthy of anything new.

One evening, almost two years after I started seeing my counsellor, I was celebrating with a friend who had just finished her finals at university. She had invited me to go out for a meal and I had accepted, having made sure that I would be able to have coffee only. To my surprise, I found myself ordering a salad! If someone had asked me to order a salad it would have been different. I would have fought it and then felt very guilty. But this just came naturally. My friend could hardly believe her eyes when I ate the meal, enjoyed it and was full of thankfulness to God.

Things progressed from there. I found that I was able to eat more, and the guilt and the self-reproach slowly disappeared. Even the fact that I was gaining weight didn't seem important any longer. The truth of God's word had penetrated from head knowledge to heart knowledge. I knew in my heart that God loved me, and this changed how I felt about myself. God's word and my relationship with him had broken the power which Satan had held over my life.

I think that when I surrendered my life to God, I had come to the end of myself. I gave my will to him, and then he was able to help me. Nobody can force another person to come to this point, but I often advise people to replace the thoughts they have about themselves, with what God says in the Bible, for that is the real truth which brings freedom (John 8:32).

I got married seventeen years ago. I had absolute assurance that it was the right thing to do, and the marriage has been a very happy one, but at thirty-nine years of age it was a big step. My husband knew about my history and my anorexic tendencies. He was very patient and understanding, although it must have been hard for him when I had times of depression and perhaps did not eat as much as he wanted me to. However, we have grown closer together, and he is a great strength and help. I was prescribed the anti-depressant Prozac, which I still take, and this helps me withstand my occasional depression.

My husband is sixteen years older than I am, and retired twelve years ago. He was keen for me to give up work as well. I found that idea very difficult, as I enjoyed my job very much and was worried that I might become depressed again if I gave it up. After praying and talking about this for three years, God changed my attitude. I wanted to spend more time with my husband, and I realised that this was more important than my work. I retired two years ago, still feeling rather anxious about this new stage of my life. God has provided wonderfully for me. Just before I gave up my job I was asked if I would do voluntary editorial work for a journal. There were problems with the publication schedule which was running about six months behind, and so it was something I could get my teeth into. I was provided with a computer, printer and fax machine, so that I could work from home. My former boss also gave me a desk to work from in the office when I needed it. This means that I am now able to work mainly from home and still go into the office about once a week to collect mail and do any necessary work there. The job keeps me in contact with former colleagues. I enjoy the work, which is certainly stimulating, and yet I have more time at home to spend with my husband and do other things. I can hardly believe how good God has been to me.

For many years now I have eaten normally, but not excessively. My weight is not high, but is healthy. I enjoy food, and I can eat as good a meal as my husband. God has set me free! The old bondage is gone.

10

Tracy – Treatment Centres

When I was fifteen, I became pregnant, and had the pregnancy terminated. Because of my age, my parents had to give permission for the termination. My father completely stopped speaking to me for six months after this, to show his disapproval. Also I was placed in a hospital ward with people who had experienced miscarriages, and that made me feel even worse about having an abortion; I felt very guilty. Then I was ill after coming out of hospital.

I had put on some weight while I was pregnant, and I did not lose it all after the abortion. I was told that I was looking chubby and my mother and I decided that we would both diet. My weight went down and down, and I developed anorexia nervosa – I ate very little, and I exercised obsessively.

I married the father of the baby I had aborted, but the marriage only lasted three years. After getting divorced, I met Dave, who is now my husband. He has supported me in a very real way over the years and has sought help for me. Dave and I saw a psychiatrist together for a year. My parents then very reluctantly agreed to join us for family therapy sessions; I found it helpful to have an opportunity to voice my frustration and sadness about my father's reaction to me – I had been feeling very hopeless about the situation. My mother cried throughout the sessions, and my father denied that he had stopped talking to me. While the sessions were difficult, on the whole the therapy was helpful.

Following the family therapy, I managed to gain enough

weight to be allowed to receive treatment for infertility. I had not really overcome the anorexia, but I desperately wanted to have a baby, and I channelled everything into this. I became pregnant and Matthew was born seven weeks prematurely. Giving birth was a tremendous shock to my system. I had to have a D & C which brought back all my memories about the termination. I found that difficult to deal with, but I managed to carry on from day to day.

Becoming a mother did not solve all my problems. In fact, I developed a new difficulty, as I felt I had lost my identity as an individual, and I had become just a mother. In time, I decided to return to work, so that at least I would have some sense of myself as a separate person from Matthew. However, I was not able to work full-time for very long. When my husband joined the police force, I started to work part-time so that I could also fulfil my duties as a mother and wife. I felt pretty worthless at this time, and whenever I felt under stress, I responded by eating less.

Eventually, I hit rock bottom. It was near Christmas, and for some reason I decided to go to church. There was a carol concert on and for once, I found a sense of peace. Not long after this, I decided to become a Christian, and then my husband also became a Christian. We found some very supportive friends. When I had an opportunity to go to Lourdes I grabbed the chance, as I had heard that many people had been healed when they visited this special place of pilgrimage. I didn't go in order to find healing for my anorexia, but I went in the hope of putting to rest my feelings about the baby I had aborted.

To my disappointment, when I arrived there I discovered that because someone else had paid for me to go there, I was expected to help out, rather than to receive help for myself. I found it hard to say 'no', as I had a real drive to help others, and so I spent the time there pushing people about in wheelchairs. On several occasions I almost collapsed, as I was still very underweight.

By the time I got back home, I felt very weak. I was referred back to the psychiatrist who had provided our family therapy, years earlier. He was shocked when he saw how ill I looked, and he recommended that I be admitted to hospital. I felt so ill that I agreed to this, and I spent five weeks in a room on my own, separated from the patients on the wards. All my clothes were taken away, which felt like a punishment, and I was told I could have them back as a reward if I gained weight. I did put on weight, but I felt degraded, and it did not solve any of the underlying problems.

Eventually I gained enough weight to be discharged from hospital, but I knew that the underlying problems had not been addressed. After a year of trying to cope on my own, I started to see a very good counsellor. She was able to help bring some healing to my life, under the layers of problems which had been peeled off. She recommended that I take 'time out' from my busy life to focus on my recovery. Although I was a bit nervous about doing this, I agreed, and I went to Kent to stay at a centre for people recovering from addictions.

The centre used a Twelve Step model. This is the approach used by Alcoholics Anonymous and several other organisations. It encourages people to take twelve specific steps towards recovery from whatever their problem might be. The first steps involved facing up to my problems, and admitting that I needed help. For me, this was not as easy as it sounds, as I had been trying to deny that I had a problem. There were ten other steps to be guided through after this, including, in step six, being entirely ready to have God remove all my defects of character. The whole process took much longer than I had anticipated. I had only expected to spend eight weeks at the centre, but I eventually stayed for sixteen. Although I made a lot of progress during that time, this happened in a very sheltered environment, which was an oasis where I was protected from the daily responsibilities, decisions and hassles of normal life. When I returned home, I found it difficult to continue the progress I had been making.

Two years after leaving the centre, it was obvious that I still had eating problems. I was thirty-five years old, and had lived with an eating disorder for twenty years. Someone at my church recommended that I visit Burrswood, a Christian medical centre in Kent, where people with medical or emotional problems can receive help. People usually stay there for a period of two weeks, although in special instances they may stay longer. My initial reaction was to think that I could not afford to go there, and that they would not accept me anyway because of my low weight. However, when my mother told me how worried she was feeling about me, and encouraged me to try Burrswood, I decided I should consider it. My doctor actively supported me in going there, and so I agreed to.

I was terrified that it would be like the hospital where I had felt punished and stripped bare. That fear soon vanished when I arrived and the love and presence of God totally overwhelmed me. The team of Christians working there showed a great deal of love for each person in their care, in stark contrast to the indifferent attitude of staff I had encountered in hospital. This in itself was not enough to drive out my second fear, which was that my time at Burrswood would be too short for any difficulties to be resolved, and that I would again be left like a peeled onion, with some of my layers of defences torn off me, but without time for healing to take place.

I had booked to stay at Burrswood for two weeks, and to spend time with both a counsellor and a chaplain. I felt abandoned and nervous when I was not able to see them straight away – I wanted to get on with the process. When at last I did meet the counsellor, I allowed some of my anger and fear to surface. I challenged her, 'How do you expect to achieve anything significant with me in two weeks, when I've had these problems for twenty years?' I couldn't see how we could do anything in that space of time. She did not appear to be put off by my question, and replied very calmly, 'We actually have somebody here who is an unseen presence, and you will be surprised at what he can achieve in two weeks.'

This turned out to be completely true. I was amazed to discover that the most powerful experiences in my thirty-five years of life took place during my short stay there. Years of therapy could not have brought about the changes which were achieved during those two weeks. When I met the chaplain, the reason for my going to Burrswood became very clear. It was as if God had already told her exactly what she needed to know about me. This removed another of my fears, which was that she would delve into everything which was painful in my life, and ask lots of difficult questions. She did not do that at all. She was a hospital chaplain who had held services for babies who had been terminated, miscarried or still-born, in addition to her usual duties as a chaplain. This meant that she had a deep understanding of the emotional pain which I still carried concerning the termination of the pregnancy, and she did not need to ask me to describe it. She knew where I was coming from. I felt God's love in providing just the right person to help me.

The chaplain asked me to name my unborn baby. I called her Laura Rose. A Communion service was held for the baby, a service to lay her to rest. I felt physical pain which was similar to the pain I had felt after the termination – something powerful was happening in me. After the service the pain disappeared, and I had a sense of peace with God and with myself which I had not known for twenty years. At last, I felt free to move on in my life. Up until that point, although I was a Christian, I had not really forgiven myself for having the abortion. Since then I have been able to both forgive myself and to accept God's forgiveness. I realise that I am loved by God and accepted by other people. I had never really believed that God could work so powerfully and bring about such a major change in my life.

Although that was the turning point in my recovery, I was not completely 'whole' yet. I went back to Burrswood for a follow-up counselling session, which highlighted some other areas in my life which I needed to look at. The physical consequences of my anorexia were also explained to me. For example, I learned that I had developed osteoporosis (brittle bones) as a result of years of hormonal imbalance and malnutrition caused by my eating disorder.

This stay at Burrswood gave me the courage, for the first time, to seek help specifically about my eating, and I went to see a nutrition consultant. I also started to see a psychotherapist, who helped me look at my fears. He showed me that I did not need to keep on dwelling on the past. I could look forward. Reading relevant books helped me to make further progress.

Unfortunately, the progress was short-lived. Soon after this I hit an all-time low, physically and emotionally. I felt more depressed than I had ever felt before, and my body was totally exhausted. Each morning I dreaded the day ahead. Everyday activities daunted me; even the simplest tasks overwhelmed me. After taking my son to school, doing a few household chores and perhaps making a couple of phone calls, I would have to return to bed to rest for an hour.

Burrswood had offered me the opportunity to return for further help, but they were unable to offer long-term treatment. I was extremely grateful for the help which I had already received from them, but this time I thought that I needed support for a longer period, so that I could get back on my feet. I felt I had to get help quickly, as my weight was dangerously low. It was frightening to acknowledge how ill I was, but I also found it strangely reassuring to admit to myself just how much I needed help.

I contacted a Twelve Step clinic. After many letters and phone calls, I managed to secure a funded place there. This clinic dealt not only with anorexia, but also with other forms of addiction, such as dependency on alcohol, drugs, gambling and smoking. The stumbling-block for me was that they only accepted people who weighed at least six stone. I was far below that weight, and could not manage to gain weight at home. My lifestyle and my fear of food and weight gain were still pushing me down.

I felt that time was running out, and I arranged to visit Burrswood again. I had been having great difficulty sleeping, because of the side effects of the medication which I was on, and this was adding to my exhaustion. The doctor changed my medication, which was helpful. However, while I was there, I developed some flu-like symptoms. Alone in my room at night, I thought that I was dying. I prayed, 'Lord, take me now.' Then I realised that this prayer was selfish, and I added, 'If it is your will.' It wasn't God's will to take me that night. I slept, and the next morning I woke without pain. I felt as if a tremendous weight had been lifted from me – there was a real feeling of peace. The staff at Burrswood pray for each person who visits the centre, and I am sure that God answers their prayers.

While staying at the centre, I began to experience flashbacks and vivid memories of being abused as a young girl. These pictures filled my dreams, and intruded into my conscious thoughts. The chaplain and counsellor helped me through this difficult time, supporting me as I tried to come to terms with my past. Because of my great need for help, I was able to stay at Burrswood for five weeks this time. I was not forced to eat, but the counsellor and the chaplain helped me to look at my diet and my activity levels. With their loving support, I was able to gain a little weight.

I spent the mornings resting. The fact that I was able to rest without feeling guilty was a miracle in itself, and certainly helped me physically. Church services were held on the grounds, and I attended as many as I could, hungering to be fed spiritually; I went to two or three each day. Three or four times a week there were special healing services, attended by many visitors.

I also enjoyed walking in the beautiful grounds. The whole area seemed to be surrounded by an overwhelming sense of peace and love, which I could not understand or describe.

My time at Burrswood gave me the inner strength and determination I needed to carry on, and I was very grateful for the loving support I received there. I felt that God had given me a second chance. He did not want me to die yet; he had a purpose for me. I did not know what, or why, I just knew that it was so.

When I returned home, I realised that the centre with the Twelve Step programme, which treated multi-addictions, was not the answer for me. I consulted my doctor again, as he had been tremendously supportive, especially in supporting my applications to go to Burrswood. Much to my relief, he agreed that a specialist unit for people with eating disorders had the best chance of helping me move towards complete recovery. He suggested that I could investigate the type of treatment offered at various units, and I could decide which I felt was the best option for me. General Practitioners need to apply for special funding when they want to send patients for treatment in specialist centres outside the area in which they live. This is called an Extra Contractual Referral (ECR). My GP promised that he would fully support my application for an ECR, wherever I chose to go for treatment.

My weight was extremely low at this point, and I don't know how I found the energy to visit the different clinics, but somehow I managed to travel around England, visiting six specialist units to find out what sort of treatment they offered. I wanted to make sure that I would receive the treatment which was right for me, as I felt this might be my last chance of recovery. Having visited these six units, I decided that Riverdale Grange in Sheffield was likely to provide the best help for me. The application procedure was far from straightforward, but my application was finally accepted, and I travelled to Sheffield for treatment.

I am pleased that I chose Riverdale Grange. Although the patients all had eating disorders, and the approach aimed to remove the fear around food, this was not the only goal of the programme. A 'holistic' approach was used, caring for the whole person. The aim was to help us in many areas of life, such as socialising, dealing with difficulties, and building up confidence and self-esteem. Every week there were opportunities for individual counselling, group therapy, art therapy, aromatherapy, relaxation sessions, and time in the kitchen. We were also asked to participate in various chores, such as laying tables, washing up, and washing our own clothes. This helped to prepare us for 'living in the outside world' in due course, so that we did not become institutionalised. It might sound like hard work, and that's because it *was* hard work, in more ways than one. It was challenging, and many tears were shed, but I was glad I was there.

I found the staff very supportive. They were firm but kind, and extremely caring. Riverdale aimed to offer a relaxed family atmosphere, and I found their approach different to other clinics which I had visited. Although it might not suit everyone, I felt that it was right for me. During my time at Riverdale, I felt that I was beginning to live again. We played games together, which helped to break my habit of isolating myself from other people; I learned to socialise – I sometimes even had fun! Fun had been missing from my life for a long time, so this was a major sign of progress.

After I had spent a few months at Riverdale, I began to go home to Hertfordshire each weekend. This meant a lot of travelling, but it helped to bridge the gap between being a patient and resuming responsibility for myself. My husband and I started to see a counsellor together, and our relationship grew stronger. We realised that my stay at Riverdale had been very worthwhile. It had helped me become willing to mix with others, to try different things, and to actively participate in life, rather than just surviving from one day to the next.

My attitude towards food had improved greatly, although my food choice was still restrictive. I had over twenty years of bad habits to change. I think that if I had gone for help much earlier, I could have changed more easily. But generally I was able to get on with my life, and not get bogged down with problems day after day. I met to pray with a prayer partner and I found this mutual prayer support very important, as I had learned that I could not do everything alone, and that it was OK to reach out to other people. I knew that if I had a bad day, it was usually because I had not listened to God. Even setbacks could be useful, as they reminded me to take time to turn to God.

Since my first stay at Burrswood, when my voyage of recovery really began, my life has changed for the better in many different ways. For example, before then I had no real appreciation of nature. I was too caught up with my problems to notice the smell of a flower, or the colour of a butterfly. Now I have a heightened appreciation of God's world, and I am able to enjoy the beauty and variety of nature. I have developed a great love of art and music, which I never had before. I am learning to read music and to play a musical instrument for the first time in my life. This is something which I always wanted to do, but until recently I never had the courage to try. In addition to this, I have changed from never wanting to read the Bible, to finding that there aren't enough hours in the day to read it and other Christian books. I have also grown more confident, especially through doing some voluntary work with the Red Cross. Life is no longer something which I just endure, it is something I truly enjoy.

I would like to encourage other people who have struggled for years with difficulties, to have hope and keep going. God loves each individual. 'He loves you just the way you are, but he loves you too much to leave you that way.' He has demonstrated that in my life. He has given me the strength to take part in life, with my family. I have learned that the more healed I am, the more help I can be to others. I know that God 'comforts us in all our troubles, so that we can comfort those in any trouble with the comfort we ourselves have received from God' (2 Corinthians 1:4).

11

Alison – Writing Prayers

My brother used to say that I was the only girl he knew who ate three proper meals a day. I had a normal, healthy appetite. I only missed meals when I was feeling depressed. At such times I would become very quiet and lethargic, literally not wanting 'to be', and I would avoid people. I had one major experience of depression when I was seventeen, but I was not formally diagnosed as suffering from depression until I was twenty. At that point I was signed off work for two months, and I was given anti-depressants. I also received help from my pastor.

Over the course of the next few months I overcame the depression. At the end of the year I was offered a job as nanny for a three-year-old girl named Zoe, who had Down's syndrome. I was given sole charge of her while her mother was at work, and I quickly grew to love her. I was delighted with the job, and I started to enjoy life again, and to feel better about myself. It came as a shock to me when I discovered, after I had looked after Zoe for nearly a year, that I was expected to settle her into a nursery and then leave. The agency who had recruited me had not told me that the job was only temporary, and I had expected that I would work with Zoe for much longer, and watch her grow up. I didn't complain about the agency, though. I simply pretended that I had known all along that the job was temporary; nor did I allow myself to appear sad about leaving Zoe, although in reality it affected me deeply.

I immediately started looking for another job, to distract me from my feelings of loss. Since childhood, I had felt that the Lord had called me to be a missionary in Brazil. In preparation for this, I wanted to do some full-time Christian work in Britain first. I applied to a Christian organisation, and was accepted for voluntary work in London for one year. It was during this year, when I was twenty-two years old, that I developed anorexia nervosa.

The voluntary work involved living with twenty others, which I found difficult. I have always liked to spend time on my own, but in this busy hostel it was hard to find a corner where I could be alone to read, or even just think. I also struggled with the actual tasks which were expected of me. In particular, I felt very uncomfortable about going round houses telling people about God. I now know that this is simply not my gift, and so I would choose not to do it. However, at the time I felt that God must want me to do this door-to-door evangelism, and so I forced myself to keep going.

Because I was unhappy about the living conditions and the work, I started eating less, and sometimes ate nothing at all. I did not like participating in group meals as I felt nervous when I was surrounded by so many people. I was the only vegetarian, and my meals were often forgotten, inadequate or burnt. I gradually stopped eating proper meals, and became weak and unable to concentrate. In a sense that was a relief, because my mind could no longer dwell on my failings, as I had to put all my energy into simply surviving. I could also blame my lack of food for any failure or difficulties in my work.

It was at this point that a Christian friend, Jane, pointed out to me that I was anorexic. As we prayed together, I told the Lord that I did not believe this diagnosis, and that if it was true, he would need to show me. That weekend I went into a bookshop, and out of all the books in the shop, the first one which I noticed was *Puppet on a String* by Helena Wilkinson. I turned to the back cover, wondering what it was about. I was amazed to read that it was about the author's experience of anorexia nervosa. As I read the cover, I turned cold, believing that God had given me an answer to my prayer – and it was an answer which I did not want.

I bought the book and immediately began to read it avidly, even in the bath. I identified with the experiences Helena described, and I realised that my behaviour was typical of that of someone with anorexia. I felt that God was speaking to me gently, as a concerned Father, asking, 'Alison, what are you doing to yourself?'

Because I wanted to please God, I started trying to eat more. Unfortunately, by this time the anorexic habits were becoming automatic, and I found it hard not to continue sliding down the slippery slope. My thoughts and feelings about food made it difficult for me to eat. Even though part of me longed to eat, I felt too afraid and guilty to allow myself to consume as much as I needed.

It was not long before my team leaders knew that I was anorexic, and they tried to help. I was too tired to continue with the door-to-door evangelism, so they gave me a job in a Christian bookshop instead.

Throughout this time, Jane was a great support to me. She had known someone else who had suffered from anorexia, and so she was aware of the symptoms, and understood where I was coming from. She was often able to infer what I was thinking, and to challenge the thought patterns which were unhelpful to me. For example, on one occasion she noticed that I was watching her while she ate a snack. She commented, 'You are wondering how I can justify eating this. Well, I don't have to!' Another time she commented that although I thought I looked good in my tight T-shirt and jeans, the reality was that I looked horribly thin. It was a shock to hear this, and I began to cover up my shape, rather than showing it.

At another point, I was unable to work for a few weeks, because I was too ill. I felt guilty about accepting free accommodation from the organisation without giving them anything in return. When I told Jane how I felt about this, her response was to ask me, 'How long have you been a volunteer?' to which I replied, 'Six months.' Then she continued, 'How long have you been away from the work?' I answered, 'Two weeks.' Her simple questioning helped me to see that I had been believing a lie – I was not a self-centred person who was taking from the charity and being unwilling to give. Indeed, I had given them a lot over the six months.

Jane also explained some of the physical symptoms of anorexia which I was experiencing. I noticed that my face was changing; she said my cheeks were looking hollow. I observed that my hair seemed different; she said 'You are losing your hair.' She told me the truth, in a loving manner. She never laughed at the fact that my clothes were becoming too big for me, as other people did. She knew how serious my condition was becoming. She prayed with me, and held me when I cried. I was able to confide in her. Sometimes she shouted at me, and at other times she reasoned with me. She helped me to see the reality of what was happening. She was firm, but I always knew that she cared for me.

I went to see a psychologist at Guy's Hospital, for counselling sessions. During one session I heard her ask a question, and I looked out at the window, then looked back, thinking, 'Does she really want an answer?' I could not concentrate on what people said. I had no energy to hold a conversation. No energy to laugh or to cry. It was at this session that the psychologist told me that she was very concerned about me, and she stated how many calories I should eat each day. She also informed me that if I got below a certain weight, I would have to be admitted into hospital. I did not know anything about calories at the time, and so I bought a book about them, the book also gave information about the amount of fat contained in food. I panicked when I read these numbers, and for a while I started eating even less, as I tried to reduce the amount of fat which I was eating.

At this low point I went home to see my parents, who were worried about me. Initially we tried to act as if nothing was wrong, but we could not keep up that pretence. My mother asked me, 'Don't you want to live?' After a pause, I answered, 'No.' I had reached the stage where life was too much effort, and I wanted to give up.

My mother found this hard to accept, and she asked my father to take me out for a drive in the car. We drove along in silence. After a while he pulled over to the side of the road. When I told him that my only reason for living was God, he replied softly, 'That is good enough – then live for him.' The words sunk in, and after this I tried to eat more, for a while.

However, my idea of how much food was 'sufficient' was very distorted, and I continued losing weight. Anorexic thoughts and behaviours had become second nature to me. Saying to someone with anorexia 'Why don't you just eat?' is like saying to a depressed person, 'Snap out of it!' – if they could, they would, but it's not that easy. I spent a week with a family who were able to offer me love, support and encouragement, and I ate a bit more while I was with them. But when I left, I lost weight again. I went back to them for a second time, but then I realised that the problem was mine, and nobody else could make me better without me working hard at it myself. I knew that it was not going to be easy to recover.

Not only was I eating minimal amounts, but I was also exercising a lot, to burn up calories. One day I felt very weak after a long walk, and I bought a cup of tea to give me the energy to get home. It tasted lovely. As I slowly drank it, allowing the hot liquid to warm my cold body, God reminded me of Jesus' words, '. . . how much more will your Father in heaven give good gifts to those who ask him!' (Matthew 7:11). God knew that it would take a long time for me to recover, and he was patient with me, gently reminding me of his presence, and his desire for me to be well.

My doctor kept an eye on my weight. Then one day my

team leader noticed that I was openly pleased that I had lost weight. He began to reprimand me, telling me about a girl he had known who had died from gangrene. He was trying to warn me that illnesses can go too far and lead to death. I wanted to cry, in order to make him stop talking to me in this way, but although I felt sad, no tears would come. He told me that if I would not listen, the illness would take over. I stood facing him, not saying anything, but as he spoke to me, I promised myself, 'I *am* going to eat, and this illness is *not* going to take over – whatever he says!' Anger welled up from deep inside, and rose up in me until I shouted at him to shut up! This took us both by surprise, as I had not shown any emotion for months, and certainly not anger. I ran downstairs, and ate a whole plate of risotto, to the astonishment of the girl who had prepared it. That day I reached my recommended calorie intake, for the first time.

I have strong willpower and up until this point I had used it to conquer feelings of hunger. Now, I decided to use my determination in a different way – to fight against the anorexia. I was determined to eat sufficient calories to start gaining weight. At mealtimes I imagined Jesus sitting opposite me, wanting me to eat, and I ate to please him. After meals I often felt bloated and guilty, and I would sit on my bed and read from my Bible. I usually read Psalm 139 and Isaiah 43.

I apologised to the team leader for shouting at him – after all, his words had helped me realise that I had to change. The youth leader of the organisation also tried to help me. He asked me to carry a chocolate bar with me at all times, in the hope that I would eat a little of it occasionally. He was in contact with my psychologist. He made it a condition of my stay that I ate the number of calories she had specified, and ate half a bar of chocolate on Saturdays. He threatened that he would personally drive me home if I failed to do this. These guidelines were laid down lovingly and I felt safe with them. I wanted to continue my work in London, and I knew that he would carry out his threat if I failed to follow the guidelines. If I had not already been on my way to recovery, the guidelines would not have been enough to make me eat, but because I had already taken some steps forward, they helped me continue making progress.

I needed a great deal of love while I was getting better, as it was hard to face reality without having anorexia to numb the pain. I had built up a lot of anorexic rituals which had made me feel safe around food, such as only eating on my own, always eating from a bowl, and eating only cold food or foods with lots of chilli in. I needed to break these rituals and learn to eat normally again. I practised talking to people at mealtimes, and I tried to concentrate on the conversation and not just on the food.

By the time I finished my year as a volunteer, I was definitely making progress in overcoming the eating disorder. I then spent a year back at home with my parents, and they helped me continue my recovery. My mother had read lots of books about eating disorders, and had gathered information on vegetarian food, to help me. I also started attending a self-help group. Unfortunately, it was run by people who still had eating disorders themselves which made me want to continue having symptoms so that I could feel part of the group – I did not continue with them.

Before starting my year in London, I had received some Christian counselling, so when I went to live at home again, I decided to have more sessions. This time I met with a different counsellor. We met for ten sessions, during which we talked mainly about experiences from my past, and we looked at the causes for the anorexia. As I got better, I had to face the problems which I had retreated from when I had anorexia, and the counsellor helped me to do this. In addition, I was helped to cope with recovery itself, including responding to people who said, 'You look well.' I had been afraid that this meant that I was looking fat. I learned to tell myself that this was not what they meant – rather, they were complimenting me, as I had started to look human again!

Something else which I found very helpful was writing down prayers. I had first done this when I was seventeen. No one suggested it to me, but it seemed natural to write down my feelings, telling God what was going on in my life. My emotions were very strong and I was thinking deeply and I found that by writing down my thoughts as prayers, they began to make more sense to me.

While I was anorexic, I continued to express myself to God by writing down my prayers, as well as writing poems. My mind tended to drift when I was not writing, and I found that I could concentrate better when I prayed if I wrote down my prayers. I found it hard to communicate with people when I felt sad, but writing prayers provided an outlet for my emotions, and helped me to clear my mind. I was able to lay before God how I felt, trying to be completely honest with him, like David was in the Psalms which I loved to read. Often, by the end of the prayer I was able to see a way ahead, or to hear God answering me. When things felt difficult, I would refer back to the prayers and poems which I had written previously. They helped me remember what God had already taught me, and the answers he had given me. Writing prayers regularly over the years helped me to carry on. I clung to this communication with God, as a means of survival during the difficult times. An example of a prayer I wrote while I was ill was:

Dear Father,
What is happening? Where do I go from here? Today I had an average meal which I enjoyed, and then I walked miles to try and get it out of my system. Neither was it a leisurely stroll. I was exhausted when I got in and I fell on my bed, hot and perspiring, but no tears came to my eyes.

I saw the tourists as I sped by. They seemed happy. I saw a young child with a chocolate bar. Her mum tried to take it from her and she quickly moved it out of her mum's reach. Food teases, it jests and then, when it has put you at ease, it bites.

Lord, I know I need your help, but I fear letting go. I want both you and a small me. Have mercy upon me. I'm lost. Turn my proud head before it gets too late.

While I was in the grips of anorexia, I felt that I was not able to promise God anything. I knew that God wanted me to eat, but I found it painfully difficult. Yet even in the deepest darkness, I never doubted God's love for me. I felt that he was with me as my loving heavenly Father, encouraging me to get better, and never condemning me or giving up on me. I expressed this in one of my poems:

God loves me.
He loves me when I don't get things right.
He loves me when I am angry.
He loves me when I am sad.
He loves me when I feel no-one does.
He loves me when I'm not doing anything for him.
He loves me when I've sinned.
He loves me when I'm hurt.
He loves me when I feel inadequate.
He loves me when I can't sleep.
He loves me when I don't think he does.
He loves me when I don't feel so clever.
He loves me when I just want to run away.
He loves me when I don't know my Bible as I should.
God loves me when I've hurt others.
God loves me when I can't live up to my standards.
God loves me as a vegetarian.
God loves me when I eat.
God loves me when I don't eat.
God loves me when I'm looking for love.

God loves me when I'm nervous.
God loves me when all is strange to me.
God loves me when I don't love myself.
Unconditional love.
Thank you Father.

Romans 8:35–39; Romans 5:6; John 3:16

I had been attending a church where people did not talk much about their feelings, and I found this difficult. So I left that church for a time, and started attending my father's church, where I felt more accepted, and free to talk about my experiences. I had been crying out for love at the same time as I was retreating into my eating disorder. The genuine love which I received from people in this church was able to reach me. It took me a long time to work through my anorexia, but slowly and surely I made progress. One sign of progress came when I had the courage to attend an Alpha course. This was a series of meetings introducing the basics of the Christian faith, each meeting starting with a meal. The first evening I arrived for the meal, and immediately fled in panic! A pastoral worker took me into her office and calmed me down. I found it a relief to acknowledge that I found it difficult to eat in company. Having admitted my difficulty, and found that no one laughed at me because of my anxiety, I felt able to attend, and to eat the meals. This became easier each week. After the course finished I attended another Alpha course, which gave me plenty of opportunities to practise eating with other people.

Today, eight years down the line, I live in my own mobile home, with my cat. I enjoy regular contact with my family. I am able to invite people for dinner, and to go to their houses for meals as well – something I could not have imagined doing while I had anorexia. I live a fulfilling life, and find it sad when I think that I tried to end my life prematurely; my thinking at that time was certainly distorted. While I had anorexia I was unable to reason with myself or to see things clearly, as I lacked the energy even to think. Now I enjoy thinking, and I enjoy living. I love my job, as a support worker in a residential home for people with learning disabilities. I belong to a very loving church, and have many friends there. I have learned a lot about people, and the Lord has given me a desire to get to know others and to share in their lives. I continue to communicate with God, by speaking, listening and expressing myself in writing. When I have low self-worth, I remind myself that I choose to live for God, and I turn once more to Psalm 139 and Isaiah 43. My prayer for people who are suffering from eating disorders is that they will stay close to God, and will come to know that he loves them, and does not want them to be ill, but wants to help them through it. I also pray for people who are caring for someone who has an eating disorder, as I know how frustrating I could be.

I have recently fallen in love, which has caused me to think again about my body. I am determined to push forward, and to totally reject even the slightest anorexic thought which might creep back into my mind, as I know that I am more than a body. After being single for so long, this new relationship has changed many things in my life, and is an exciting new venture. God has given me many blessings. My life has meaning and purpose, and I praise God for it.

People who do not know my past would not suspect that I have suffered from anorexia. I still occasionally have 'anorexic thoughts', but when I read about people who have died from this illness, or I remember the misery it brought me, I ask God for help, and I determine that I will never again let anorexia be part of my life.

Men Who Have Recovered

12

James – Hospital Treatment and the Love of God

My father was very good with children. He built me up to believe that I could do anything and be anything, and that I was a brilliant person. When I went to secondary school at the age of eleven, however, I learned that there were a lot of people who were much better at most things than I was and I really struggled with that. My father arranged for me to be placed in a different class from my friends, so that I could make new friends, but I didn't really have the social skills to do so. I tried to re-attach myself to my old friends, but unfortunately a couple of them moved away from the area, and another one decided to join another group of friends. So I led a lonely life. I tried to hide myself in my work, and I pretended that I didn't need anyone else in my life.

I became depressed. I think this was due to a combination of causes, including social isolation and the stress of exams. Another factor was the lack of support and structure which I received from my parents. Although they loved me, they seemed unable to express that love. I felt that I hardly knew my parents, or my brother and sister. My father was very good with young children, but he seemed almost to have a fear of teenagers. He felt unable to understand them or cope with them. Consequently, from about the age of thirteen or fourteen, I became quite independent of my parents. I was beginning to feel unhappy with the way the family lived, and to some extent I wanted to be independent. It was part of growing up, but I didn't know *how* to become an adult, because my parents had backed off and were leaving me to my own devices.

I think that a few kindly teachers at my school felt sorry for me, but the school had no psychologists, counsellors or educational welfare officers. That sort of support just didn't exist at that time and for a long time, no one recognised my illness. Then, when I was fifteen, my father took me to see a doctor who said that I must be suffering from depression. I found it quite reassuring to have a diagnosis, as I hadn't realised what the problem was.

I was put on anti-depressants. Even with the medication, I felt unable to cope with school, because I was extremely depressed. I felt far removed from my classmates, who were going out to parties and generally enjoying life. I told my father that I didn't want to go to school anymore. He was not at all pleased about that, but he agreed that I could leave school as long as I did something else. I dropped out of school, but I was too ill to get a job. I lost a lot of weight at this time, and my clothes no longer fitted me.

I was referred to a psychotherapy unit for adolescents. This unit was still in an experimental stage. Young people with a multitude of different problems were treated there. We received very little information about why we were there or how long we were likely to stay, what changes we were expected to make or what might happen after we left the unit. Most of the staff were nurses, but there were also a couple of psychiatrists.

There was no one-to-one counselling, and all the therapy was done in groups. Every morning all the patients and staff met together for a large meeting with a smaller meeting every afternoon. On one evening each week we received art therapy, and on another evening there was drama therapy. These expressive therapies were intended to help us get in touch with our feelings. Some of the other young people in the unit had been referred there because they kept stealing cars or destroying property. They used to disappear at night and we didn't see them again until the next morning.

I found it difficult to adjust to the unit at first, but I think it was the right sort of treatment for me. I needed to get in touch with my feelings, because I didn't even know what a feeling was! Neither positive nor negative emotions were expressed in our family. We weren't allowed to shout or swear at anyone, and there was no hugging or kissing. In the unit I learned what it was like to receive a hug. I also learned how to make decisions, as that was something else I had been unable to do. In four months in the unit I learned what I had failed to learn in the normal way over the previous fifteen years.

While I was there, we went camping three times. I can gauge my progress by how I got on at camp. I hated the first camp. The second one I didn't mind, and by the third I was really swinging! I ended up being the chairman of the large group we had each morning. I felt I'd come a long way. I found myself eating more normally and gaining weight, because I was feeling better about myself and enjoying the world again.

After four months, I asked the staff when I could leave. Everyone seemed very vague. Eventually I insisted on an interview with my psychiatrist, who also failed to advise me about when I could leave, so in the end I discharged myself, against their advice.

I returned home a lot more expressive and decisive than I had been previously. I had changed, but nothing seemed to have changed at home. My parents were still not in touch with their own feelings. Life at home was still difficult, and I received no follow up from the unit.

While I had been in the unit we had received family therapy once a month, and my father had hated it with a vengeance. I think the staff dreaded our appointments! I found it very odd to have my parents with me in these monthly sessions, because I felt very aloof from them, and found it difficult to relate to them. I was pursuing my own course of life, and I didn't have a lot in common with them. I felt unhappy about being part of that family, and yet I had to be part of it during the family therapy sessions. The psychiatrist tried to teach us new ways to relate as a family, but we did not go along with his suggestions.

I had discharged myself because I felt ready to leave, and because I wanted to return to school. I re-sat four O-levels, which I passed, and I went into the sixth form. I found it extremely difficult to adjust. Although I had gone home at weekends while I was in the unit, during the week we had only been allowed out for twenty minutes a day, and we had seen very little of outsiders. The front door was locked, and people needed an appointment to get in. I found it strange to leave this secure, therapeutic environment and return to school. I had learned to value my own individuality. I couldn't understand why all my classmates wanted to dress alike, speak alike and do the same things. I felt they were a bit like robots, and I realised there was a disparity between us. I had no friends. Although I had developed some social skills in the unit, because I had been out of society for a long time and the other students had developed their social groups, it was hard to fit in.

In time, a female group adopted me. I felt a bit like a lap-dog, with these girls trying to look after me. I didn't feel that I really belonged in their group, or in any group. I struggled with that, and I also struggled with the pressure of exams. It dawned on me that there was no way I was going to pass them, having missed so much schooling. I wondered how I was going to manage in life. How could I achieve all the things which I was expected to achieve such as getting a job, a wife, a house, a car, success? I began to fear the future. There seemed to be no way ahead.

I had left the unit feeling good about myself, and very positive about life. Unfortunately I had returned to a situation where I received no encouragement. There was no one supporting me – not my father or mother, nobody at school, no one. I was a young man with little social education, trying to make sense of the world, and struggling on my own with my problems. My world fell down around me. Within eighteen months of leaving the unit, I became depressed again. At one stage I tried to take an overdose, but I only managed to swallow six paracetamol, and I woke up with a headache!

I rapidly lost about three stone in weight. I didn't want to eat, because I didn't want to live, so I ate less and less. The less I ate, the more preoccupied I became with food. I couldn't help thinking about it. I sat in lessons worrying about what I'd eaten at lunchtime and what I might eat in the evening. If I thought I'd eaten too much, I would eat little or nothing at my next meal. When I did eat, I ate very slowly. It would take me an hour and a quarter to get through a small evening meal. My mother would clear the food away from the table, and everyone else would go off to do other things, and I would be left trying to eat the food. My doctor gave me some appetite stimulants which I was meant to take an hour before a meal. These were useless, as I was suffering from a psychological problem, not a physical one.

I was not deliberately trying to lose weight. I didn't have much interest in my body. I weighed about six stone at that stage, and I'm 5 foot 10. I was extremely underweight, but I didn't really notice this, and I certainly wasn't concerned about how thin I had become. The children at school teased me about it, but it still didn't register with me that I was thin.

I stopped going to school, and I became phobic about going out. I became obsessed with cleanliness, and I didn't like to touch anything. I developed a form of obsessive compulsive disorder (OCD). I was prescribed tranquillisers to reduce my anxiety. It was an extremely unpleasant time. I desperately wanted to die, because I was totally controlled by the OCD, which was making me do all manner of strange things. My life was severely restricted. I could just about sit on the bed and try not to worry about things, but that was all I could do.

After I had refused to go out of the house for a month, my

father managed to take me back to the GP. This time I saw a locum doctor, who had a special interest in mental health. I was referred back to the adolescent unit, and went for an appointment there. The doctor obviously noticed how thin I was and said he might be able to re-admit me to the unit, but it depended on my weight. He took me down the corridor to the medical room and plonked me on the scales. A look of shock went over his face as he saw how little I weighed – about five and a half stone. He told me that there was no way that I could enter the unit at such a dangerously low weight; I needed to be confined to bed. He said that I could either enter a general hospital or stay at home and try to gain weight.

My dad wanted me to go into hospital, but I didn't fancy that, so I went home. My parents devised a meal structure for me. I stayed in bed most of the time, and when I got out of bed I fainted, because of the lack of food. I felt very cold all the time and I had to have an electric blanket on the bed and a sheepskin rug under the sheet to try to keep me warm.

I spent three weeks in bed at home, but I didn't put on any weight. My father got very angry with me which amazed me, as I had never known him to express anger before. Although I felt that his personality and behaviour had contributed to my illness, I also realised that he was my main hope of survival. I knew that he wanted me to go into hospital, and so I agreed to go.

I was admitted into a very large, open-plan ward. It was divided into sections, and each section had no more than eight beds. I was moved around a lot during my time in the ward, and I was often in a section on my own. I went into hospital in January and I didn't leave until August, so I was there for almost seven months. I spent nearly all of this time sitting in bed. As I had no padding I sat on a rubber ring on a sheepskin rug, but I still developed bed sores and my skin came off – I've still got the scars now.

On my first night in hospital, I looked at the medical card

at the end of my bed. It simply said, 'anorexia'. Until that point, no one had ever mentioned that word to me. Again, I was relieved to have a diagnosis, but when other patients started asking me why I was in hospital, I wished that I had a physical illness and not a psychological one. I was in a general medical ward which specialised in cardiac problems, and the other patients were all being treated for physical complaints. I was too embarrassed to tell them that I had an eating disorder.

I was set target weights to aim at, and told of privileges I would receive when I reached them. At specified weights I would be allowed to sit on a chair, walk to the toilet and walk down to the end of the corridor. At the magic weight of eight stone, I would be allowed to go home. I had no interest in the rewards, and even the thought of going home did not appeal to me. Using rewards to entice me to gain weight was pointless. I had become phobic of life, because I believed that I was never going to be able to live up to all the expectations people had of me. I would not put on weight unless something changed within me and made me want to live.

Although I lacked interest in life, my depression did lift slightly when I entered hospital. The structured, ritualistic, clean environment helped to relieve my obsessions a little. My anxiety fell, because pressure was removed from me, and less was expected of me; because I was in hospital, I no longer had to try to be 'normal', or to achieve anything. I was just left with the problem with food.

I was placed under the care of a psychiatrist who was determined to get me better without the use of medication. He took me off the tranquillisers and sleeping tablets which I had been taking. I was pleased about that.

The counselling which I received from the psychiatrist made up for the futility of the reward regime. I met with him four times every week for seven months, so it was quite intensive. That was just as well, as there was a lot to unravel. A lot of the counselling focused on my family, and it helped me tackle difficult issues. Towards the end, the psychiatrist helped me prepare for life after I left the hospital.

People might have assumed that I would put on weight very quickly when the pressures on me were removed, but I didn't. In fact, although I found the counselling helpful in sorting out my thinking, my weight dropped, to five stone two pounds. The doctors feared for my life and I was told firmly, 'If you lose half a pound more, you'll be on a drip, mate!' I didn't want that, so I managed to eat a bit more. I stopped losing weight, but I didn't gain any for four months. I was weighed twice each week, and my weight hardly changed. A lot of people became very frustrated with me. I was still scared of life, and I knew that if I put on weight I would have to leave hospital and go back home. I didn't want to face up to the expectations of life – such as making decisions, earning a living and making friends.

A combination of two things helped me get out of this rut. The catalyst was a conversation with a doctor one evening. She stood at the end of my bed, frustrated by my lack of progress, and asked if I had ever heard of Florence Nightingale. When I said that I had, she continued, 'Did you know that when Florence Nightingale came back from the Crimean War, she spent a year lying in bed?' I replied that I didn't know that. The doctor then asked, 'Do you want to spend the rest of your life lying in bed?' The question challenged me. I thought, 'No I don't. I've spent four months in bed, and this is a really naff thing to be doing.' I had just had my eighteenth birthday, in hospital, and I realised no, I didn't want to spend the rest of my life in bed. The next morning I woke up and decided to get better!

That was the catalyst, but I really don't think that someone lecturing me about Florence Nightingale would have caused such a rapid turnaround in my attitude had it not been for something else. I had been suffering from a very serious illness, and I was in danger of dying from malnutrition. Why did I recover when other people have died from this condition? I believe it was because God answered the prayers which people made on my behalf, and he turned me around. I wasn't a Christian myself at the time, but a lot of Christians knew about me, and were praying for me.

I believe that God used the doctor's comment to get through to me. It could have been anyone saying anything. It just happened to be this phrase, 'Do you want to spend the rest of your life lying in bed?', which made me think, 'No!' There must have been something which made me say 'No'. If she had said this a month earlier, I would have ignored the comment and it would not have made a blind bit of difference to my behaviour, because I wanted to avoid life, and staying in bed was a good way to do that. Something had altered within me, and the doctor's remarks caused an immediate, dramatic change in my attitude.

From that point, I put my mind to gaining weight. You've never seen anyone try so hard to put on weight! I ate everything that was given to me, and I also invented a few things of my own. I had a little book of calories, and I went through the book and decided that there was no point in eating anything which would fill me up but had few calories, like fruit and vegetables. Instead, I chose to eat high-calorie foods like chips, pizzas and meat. I asked my mother to bring me in a tub of butter, and a large pack of rich tea biscuits. I would spread the butter on the biscuits and think, 'Here we are, we've got something with a high fat content, on something with a high sugar content.' I would eat about three of these between meals. I also asked permission to get my mother to bring me in boxes of Complan, a high-calorie food supplement. I would ask the nurses for glasses of full cream milk, into which I would throw as much Complan as possible. The combination of the butter and biscuits, the Complan, and the high-calorie meals, meant that I was putting on three to four pounds a week. I rapidly reached the weight goal at which I was allowed to get out of bed, but I refused to walk around. The doctor encouraged me,

'Come on, you're allowed to go out now because you've reached your goal weight.' But I replied, 'No, I'm staying on this bed. I can't risk losing calories here, because I want to put on weight and go home'!

This radical change in my behaviour was not easy to sustain, because my stomach felt extremely uncomfortable all the time. In the evenings I used to grip the sides of the bed very tightly, because I felt so uncomfortable. But I had set my mind on getting better, and nothing was going to stop me. There were certain pleasures which came with getting better, such as regaining the ability to concentrate. When I was very low in weight I couldn't concentrate on anything, but as I regained weight I was able to watch a film on television all the way through and not miss anything, and I was able to concentrate on reading books again. In a sense, I regained an appetite for life. The first book I read was *The Hobbit*, and then I moved on to *The Lord of the Rings*, and all of Tolkien's books. The fact that I was able to touch the books meant that my obsession with cleanliness had also decreased. My conversations with visitors became a bit more sprightly. Prior to that I had been so ill that when visitors came, I sometimes couldn't speak to them at all.

As the psychiatrist continued to help me gain a better understanding of myself, I started to think more about my early childhood. I remembered that I had once had a very good sense of humour, and, being a bit of a clown, I had often been the centre of attention. I thought, 'If that's the way God made me, that's the way I should be. What has happened has just taken away my joy.' I realised that if I had been happy as a child, I could still be like that. I had the potential to change, and to become a joyful person again. I started to look forward to that.

I began to take an interest in Christian things. I asked my father to bring in my Gideon's Bible; at the front there is a list of Bible passages which can offer help when one is facing various problems, such as depression and loneliness. Although I wasn't a Christian, the Holy Spirit was drawing me to read these passages. As a child, I had been taught that the Old Testament was just a long list of parables which had never really happened, and I had thought that the Bible was irrelevant. Now, for the first time, I began to realise that the Bible was actually true and could influence my life. I started to use the Scriptures to encourage myself.

I also received encouragement from people who came to see me in hospital. I realised that people were considerate of me. The young women who had befriended me at school came to visit and people told me afterwards that they were very distressed because I looked so thin, that although they bore up in front of me, they then went home and cried. I hadn't realised that my illness was serious. I remember one man from my father's church coming in, and when he saw me there was a vivid look of relief on his face, and he said, 'You had us all worried for a moment there.' After he'd gone, I suddenly realised that I could have died; it was quite a shock when I discovered that people had considered that I might not pull through.

I spent three months regaining weight – from five stone two pounds up to eight stone. When I reached the eight stone target, I was discharged from hospital. I hadn't been outside for seven months so I felt very odd walking out of the hospital, which wasn't helped by the fact that my clothes didn't fit me any more. Also my muscles had wasted as I had not used them for seven months, so I found it difficult to walk. My vivid impression, walking down the hospital steps into the sunlight, was how warm it was, and how untidy nature was. The ward had been very ordered both in its routines and in its appearance – all the beds were identical and neatly kept, and all the furniture was the same colour. I had been used to a sterile, symmetrical environment. Now I was surrounded by God's creation, full of variety. I stared at the trees and hedgerows thinking how untidy it all looked.

Because I had taken such a long time to get better, I felt that I had been able to do it properly. The four months I spent in the adolescent unit had been a bit too rapid, and I hadn't consolidated my recovery, or all the things which I had learned. God enabled me to get better in a more complete way, by allowing me to spend those seven months in the hospital, receiving considerable input from the psychiatrist. I was determined to stay well, because the two breakdowns had been extremely unpleasant and there was no way I wanted to return to that.

I was by now past school age, which was a big help, as I no longer felt under pressure to return to school as quickly as possible. Something else which helped was that one of my close friends, who had moved away from the area, was now living near me again. His father had recently died, and so my friend was living on his own. I visited him every day and I also started to make a few other friends. They tended to be people like myself who had been through difficult times – for example, one of them suffered from schizophrenia. These were people I felt able to relate to; they were not going out to parties all the time, or trying to conform to the expectations of other people. They didn't leave me feeling inferior.

I attended out-patient appointments with my psychiatrist, which I found very helpful. These appointments occurred less and less frequently, as the psychiatrist was helping me become less dependent on him. At my last appointment I felt quite insecure, and I asked him to give me a sick-note, because I did not feel capable of working. He gave me one for six weeks, but after the six weeks were up, I still felt unable to work. So it was another couple of months before I started to look in the job centre, even though I didn't want a job. There came a point, though, months later, when I felt I really did want a job and I got part-time work, which was very basic, but it was a start. That developed into full-time employment. So I slowly progressed.

I went through a stage of rebelling against my family, and left home. For the first two months after I left, I had no contact with them at all. I didn't even phone them. Living away from them, in a shared house, gave me a great sense of achievement. I was making friends with people who might be considered distasteful. I was doing things I wouldn't do now, like getting drunk, and watching lots of horror movies. I guess I was starting to conform, doing things which I saw other people around me doing. Nevertheless, I still felt extremely lonely.

The Holy Spirit began working in my life in a more pronounced way at this point. I was twenty-one, and should have been in the prime of life, but I felt insecure, unfulfilled and empty, as though there was a bit of me missing. I started to think about God. I thought, 'The psychiatrist has done a very good job, and I'm better now, but is this all there is to life?' I was dogged by the question of what was the point of living, and I wanted to be free from my anxieties about the future. God uses negative experiences for his purposes and to bring glory to himself and to bring us to the place he wants us to be. In a sense, although the devil had kept me under his foot for several years, what he'd done to me had actually caused me to hunger after God. I was drawn to thinking very clearly that the only way to find fulfilment in life was somehow tied up with God. As I walked to work each day, I passed a church. On Sundays, I saw people being greeted very warmly as they walked in. I felt surprised, because I had never noticed people showing any expression of warmth or love to each other in the church I had attended in the past – it had seemed to be a place of intellectual discourse, with no life in it. This new church that I'd discovered, on the other hand, looked full of life. It was a bit scary, but it did appeal to me.

A Christian newspaper was pushed through my door by the people in this church, as they were pushing one through the door of every house in the city. The paper contained testimonies of ways God had practically helped people. He'd healed people, given them jobs, or given them a marriage partner. There was a picture inside of people worshipping in an expressive way. I thought 'Wow, these people have had God impact their life in such an amazing way, maybe he can do the same for me!'

A few more weeks passed by, and then I made a decision to try out this church. The Sunday I had decided to go, I overslept. When I woke up, it was pouring with rain. A little voice inside me said, 'You get yourself up and get down there to church.' I walked down the road, and on the way passed an Anglican church. I thought, 'I'll go in here instead, because it's what I know. I know the prayer book by heart, I could impress everyone.' But the little voice inside me warned, 'If you go back in there, you'll be as dead as you ever were.' So I decided to pluck up my courage and carry on up the road to the other church.

When I got to the door, I managed to avoid the hug, and I sat at the back so that no one would speak to me. It was an evangelical charismatic church, and it felt a bit spooky – it was all so new. They were praying for a baby with cancer, and I thought, 'Wow, that's really good.' I was struck by the way people related to one another, and showed love to each other. They seemed happy and caring, like a big family. I guess that was something I was hankering after, because my parents had never been able to express love through touch or words. I made a quick escape at the end of the service, to avoid coming into contact with anyone. But I went back again the next week, and I felt quite hooked on the church. I knew something amazing was going to happen in my life and I was getting quite excited about it.

A couple of weeks later I went down to the river for a walk. It was July, and the young people from the church drama group were acting in the open air. They performed a sketch called the 'Race for Life', which consists of a policeman, a vicar and a do-gooder, who are racing to get into heaven. None of them get there. That impacted me strongly – not even the vicar had got into heaven! I'd assumed that simply going to church and believing in God was enough to get you into heaven. I walked up the street afterwards, realising that I wasn't a Christian. I thought, 'Right, you've got to become a Christian, this is what will change your life.' There was a real tug-of-war going on inside me. I wondered, 'Should I do it now, or should I do it later?' I decided to put it off.

I went home; my house-mates were out. I started to clean the oven – being a typical shared house, everyone left the cleaning to someone else, so there was a lot to do. I hadn't got far with the cleaning when I thought, 'No, I've got to become a Christian now.' I didn't know how to do it, so I just confessed to God that I had lived my life my own way and made a mess of it, and I felt empty. I said to God, 'Zap me!' I wasn't sure what I was meant to say. For me, 'Zap me' expressed that I knew I needed God to come and impact me in some way. As soon as I had expressed to God my need of him and confessed my sin, he came into my life. That was the moment I became a Christian. I felt as if God had come down from heaven and totally filled me with himself. I felt very close to him and I felt great happiness.

I left the oven half cleaned, staggered into the lounge and got on my knees. I lifted my hands in the air, as I'd seen people do. What was actually happening, although I didn't know it at the time, was that God was filling me with the Holy Spirit. It was an extremely powerful experience. I closed my eyes, and I saw a picture of a wall being blasted down. It was as if the wall which had stood between me and God had come down, and I had stepped from one side to the other. I knew that God had forgiven me. I felt something which I'd never felt before. It was a knowledge that someone loved me, that someone being God. I also sensed that God was going to look after me for the rest of my life. God had in an instant taught me what love was like, and given me the sense of security which I'd hungered after all my life.

God spoke to me, not in an audible voice, but as words in

my head. He said, 'I haven't taken all your troubles away, because you're going to work things out over the coming years, so that you will learn through your experiences.' He took the loneliness and emptiness away, but in his wisdom he did not remove all my problems at once. I remember thinking, 'If anyone walks into this lounge now, they will see a choir of angels singing over me!' It was odd, because I couldn't hear or see any angels, but the experience was so vivid that I felt that anyone who walked into the room would be very aware of it.

This all happened within the space of about two minutes. After this, I got up and ran into my bedroom and picked up the Bible which I had been given as a child. It had never meant much to me, but I opened it, and flicked quickly through the pages, jumping from one place to another. Every verse my eye fell on appeared to have been written just for me. It was as if it had my name printed on it. I thought that was quite astonishing, because it was a very old Bible. It wasn't even a modern translation, and yet it seemed completely relevant.

I believe that God had used the medical professionals to help me recover physically, and then had chosen his time to come in and meet my deeper needs. He filled the gap in my life, and left me feeling fulfilled. This was what I needed to ensure that my healing was complete and sustained. He gave me an assurance of his love for me, and he provided a sense of security, which dealt with the root cause of my illness.

I continued to attend the church, and I learned a lot about healthy human relationships there. Unlike some churches, this was one where people expressed feelings towards one another. That helped me a lot. I still tended to avoid the huggers at the door, but I did learn how to hug people whom I knew well.

It's now more than eleven years since I became a Christian. I believe that I have completely recovered from my eating disorder. I'm still not very heavy, I only weigh about nine stone, but my weight is stable. I have tried to gain weight, but I find it difficult to do so, so I accept myself as I am. Many people in this culture have a love–hate relationship with food. Some people eat more than they need, and others eat less. I feel relaxed around food now. I don't like to rush my meals although sometimes I have to – I rush home from work, open a can of ravioli, pour it down my neck, and then rush out to do something else. But I much prefer to take meals leisurely and enjoy them. As a young person I found my mother's cooking very uninteresting. It has been said, rather unkindly, that my mother's aim in life was to extract all taste from her cooking! It's unfair to say that, but my parents are on a low cholesterol diet, and their food seems tasteless to me. When I visit them, I come away gasping for a bag of crisps or a chocolate bar! I like to give myself treats, and I choose foods which I enjoy.

These days I'm glad to be alive. I think that if I wasn't a Christian, I would still be searching for a reason for living. I would probably run after as many pleasures as I could cram into my life, and spend all my money on alcohol. Thankfully, I've discovered a much greater source of contentment, through my relationship with God. I occasionally have days when I feel flat, but I pray about it, and that brings me through. I have regained my sense of humour. I've noticed that it does hide when I'm under stress, but on the whole I manage to maintain a keen sense of humour, which can exasperate my colleagues!

I am happily married, and I have strong feelings of love for my wife and my parents. My relationship with my parents has improved greatly. The first time I gave my mother a hug, she was so surprised that she nearly fell down. I think she blossomed when I began to express my feelings. I spend about seven days a year visiting them. I feel quite sad for my father, as he has had a couple of breakdowns and is now on anti-depressants himself. I sometimes wonder whether it was supporting me in my illness which caused his breakdowns. He visited me every day while I was in hospital, which must have been a huge sacrifice for him. I thank God that I'm not carrying a burden of guilt about this, as that wouldn't help anyone. I think it is quite likely that he was ill himself prior to my illness. He has always had trouble expressing his feelings, because that is how *his* father was and he rarely talks about his parents. When I was a young boy, dad wanted me to do great things. I don't know whether he's proud of me or not, although I think he probably is. That doesn't matter much to me now – I've learned that God's approval is all that matters.

I have a lot in common with my father. I think that when he retires, he will cheer up and be able to come off his medication. I expect that we'll get to know each other better then. I can just imagine us in our old age, sitting in armchairs like two peas in a pod, and getting very close. My mother and I already have quite a good relationship, but I think I'll grow closer to both parents when my father retires.

As far as my self-esteem goes, I feel quite good about myself, although I occasionally have moments of feeling inadequate. I try not to compete with other people at work. If one of my colleagues gets a difficult piece of work to do, I sometimes wish that I was doing that job, and competition creeps in. As a Christian, I don't want to be comparing myself with others, and if I feel inadequate for a moment, I talk to God about it. God knows what he's doing and he's not going to give me a major piece of work to do when he wants me to be spending time doing something else.

God is able to turn around the work of the devil, and use it for good. I am now a lay pastor of a church, and people come to me with their problems. If someone tells me they are feeling depressed, I am able to say that I have also felt depressed. People who assume that church leaders can cope with everything and never have any difficulties, seem to find it easier to relate to me when they know that I have also had problems. God has given me an understanding of people, and I am able to use this in my ministry.

I believe that God gives us tasks which stretch us. To be honest, there are times when I'd love to just go home in the evening, lock the door, and watch TV with a beer in my hand. But God stretches me by giving me the opportunity to care for others. Sometimes I find it difficult to be compassionate. I can be tempted to compare other people's problems to my own severe illness, and think, 'That's nothing, why worry about not having a job for a few weeks, you can claim housing benefit.' My wife has pointed out to me that I can be hard-hearted. I sometimes have to be hard in my job, as a social worker, but I need compassion to be able to pray, and to show God's love to others. As a pastor, I have to get the balance right between feeling empathy, and saying, 'The best way to overcome your problem is to do this, that and the other.' I find it easier to give people advice than to offer empathy. I have to keep asking God for his love, so that I can offer it to others.

Because these things don't come naturally to me, I have to rely on God. I certainly couldn't be a lay pastor if God wasn't enabling me to do it. The thought that people are looking to me for guidance scares the life out of me at times! I am aware that at the end of the day it is only God who can help people. All I can do is help them to pray to God for an answer to their problem. If there is a little way I can help by giving someone food or money or whatever, I will do that, but usually all I can do is depend on God. The Bible says, 'When I am weak, then I am strong' (2 Corinthians 12:10). I comfort myself with those words, because I often feel weak. That's a good place to be, because if we are puffed up in ourselves, that can prevent God from working through us. The day I feel proud about my Christian work will be the day to pack it in, because I should always have a sense that I'm relying on God. I think that's great. As a child my father made me believe that I was brilliant, a superman. I crumbled when I became aware that I wasn't. With my heavenly Father I can acknowledge my weaknesses. I'm allowed to say that there are things which I'm not good at, and that from time to time I find things difficult. I've discovered that when people come to me for help, they actually like it when I admit that I don't have all the answers. I wish I did, but I can be honest and say that I don't, which is liberating.

I rarely tell people that I have had an eating disorder. I don't mind telling people that I've suffered from depression, or that I've had two nervous breakdowns, as this seems to open doors, and people then ask me to help others who are going through similar difficulties. However, most people don't seem to understand eating disorders. They think of what they've heard in the media about them, but they don't really grasp what my experience was like, so I tend not to mention it.

I did once share my story in a church, but afterwards I felt that God told me not to share it again until he asked me to, because he wanted me to look to the future and not get stuck in the past. Some people, after they have been ill, keep clinging to the past. To make a prolonged and thorough recovery, I think it's important to have a forward-looking attitude and move on. Talking about our past a lot can be a way of maintaining ourselves in a sick role. It's as if we are saying, 'I had this problem in my past, so please don't expect too much of me.' We need to get the balance right between sharing experiences in a positive way, and living in the past. It is important to work out what to tell other people, and what not to share. I need to remember the past in order to prevent me going back to it, but really I am a person who looks to the future. I'm looking forward to finding out what lies ahead.

13

Daniel – A Supportive Family and a Christian Faith

I was known as 'Big Dan' at school. When I was fourteen, I was 5 foot 7 inches tall, and I weighed over twelve stone. I was very well-built, muscular and fit. I enjoyed sports, and I represented the school, district and county as a prop-forward in the rugby team. I ate what I wanted to, without really thinking about it. Sometimes I pigged out, and sometimes I skipped meals, depending on how I felt, but it didn't really concern me. I was basically a healthy teenager.

Unfortunately, despite my ability on the rugby field, I lacked confidence and had low self-esteem. As my GCSE exams came nearer, I felt under pressure to achieve in the classroom as well as on the rugby pitch but I found it hard to keep up with my classmates. I didn't want to be a 'bad kid' and go out and get drunk, or anything like that. Instead, I devoted more and more of my attention to being fit. I became a perfectionist in sport.

I thought that I was rather short. Because I couldn't do much to change that, I tried to compensate for it by becoming fitter and fitter. I became very concerned with exercise and becoming the fittest person in the school. At first this desire was quite healthy, but it soon became obsessive.

I was studying physical education as an extra GCSE subject. Part of the course was about healthy eating, and I started to learn about fatty foods. I decided to totally avoid high-fat foods, as I associated them with being unfit, so I stopped eating chips, chocolates and sweets, and I switched to eating the foods which I considered to be 'good', such as low-fat yoghurt.

By the time I was sixteen, I had a very rigid daily routine. My day would start with an early morning jog, followed by a weight training programme. After this I sometimes had a low-calorie breakfast, but more often I skipped breakfast, as I was trying to lose weight. My parents were usually too busy to notice that I hadn't eaten.

At lunch time I would come back home and spend the lunch hour running up and down the stairs. Sometimes I forced myself to eat a sandwich or a yoghurt, but usually I went without lunch, and merely pretended that I had eaten. I would rush back to school for the afternoon classes, and as soon as they were over I would do more weight training. Afterwards I would settle down and study for a couple of hours, until dinner time.

Dinner was the most difficult meal to avoid, but I would eat as little of it as I could get away with. Sometimes I managed to hide my food and throw it away. When I had to eat with the family, I would ensure that I had a smaller portion than everybody else. I would cut my food up into tiny pieces, no bigger than crumbs, so that I would take a long time to eat, and get away with eating less.

After dinner I would study a bit more, and then exercise for a couple of hours – running up and down stairs, and using weights. I would make myself 'sweat off the fat', ensuring that every calorie which I had consumed during the day had been burned off. By the time night came I would be shattered, and quickly go off to sleep. A few hours later I'd wake up and my routine would begin again. I believed that the more I exercised and the less I ate, the better.

I didn't think that I had a problem. I thought that I was successfully controlling what I ate, and that my routine was more of a help than a burden. My exams were approaching, and the structure in my life seemed to help me focus on my studies. I believed that it was good to be disciplined, and I lived by discipline and punishment. I gained a sense of achievement from forcing myself to keep going with my exercise, or to keep studying for another hour.

My family noticed that I was losing weight, but they knew that I was trying to get fitter for the rugby team, and they thought that it was just a phase I was going through. It was around Christmas that they noticed it was becoming unhealthy. I was avoiding foods which I usually enjoyed. During the school term no one had really noticed what I was eating, but in the holidays, when I was at home more, it was more noticeable.

I would scrutinise myself in the mirror, and I weighed myself about three times a day. I was pleased every time it looked as if my weight had gone down, even if I knew the scales were just reflecting a loss of fluid. I wasn't aiming to get down to any particular weight, all that mattered was that I was losing weight. My weight had dropped from over twelve stone to eight stone at this point, and I felt cold all the time. Sometimes I made myself sick after eating, especially if I'd eaten a bit more than normal. I never really binge-ate, but if I had two extra bowls of cereal or a couple of bars of chocolate I would consider it a binge, and I would bring the food back up. I also drank loads of black coffee, as I had read that this could suppress appetite and act as a stimulant. It was very destructive, but if I heard of any trick that might help me lose weight, I tried it.

Just after Christmas, I acknowledged that something was wrong. I went to my mother and said, 'I don't know what it is, but I've obviously got a problem.' At that time I wore baggy clothes to hide my appearance, so she hadn't seen me properly. I told her how much I weighed, and she was shocked, as was my father when he caught a glimpse of my frail legs without their habitual covering of tracksuit bottoms, as I went into the bathroom one night. We went to the GP expecting her to say that I had a problem with excessive exercise. She diagnosed me as having anorexia nervosa.

I had only heard of anorexia as a faddy illness which girls could get, although I now know that men can have it too, and the behaviours are very similar for both. It took me a while to come to terms with the fact that I had anorexia. It was hard because it was not the sort of illness I could tell my friends about; I wanted to keep it to myself. I think that boys can find it difficult to talk about their problems anyway. I lied and told my friends that I'd lost weight because of a liver condition.

The GP referred me to a psychiatrist, who prescribed anti-depressants and told me to stop all my exercise. That was extremely difficult. It was like a drug addict stopping taking drugs all at once – 'cold turkey' as they call it. I had been addicted to exercising, and had used it to provide a sense of release and achievement. I had felt 'high' when I was exercising, and when I had to stop I felt very agitated. I wanted to climb the walls, but that wasn't allowed! To make matters worse, I was also gradually reducing the amount of coffee which I was drinking. The caffeine withdrawal left me feeling cranky and incredibly miserable.

It was during this time that I sat my exams. It was a very confusing time for me. By now my concentration was impaired and I couldn't think properly. After my exams there were no more lessons to attend, and my life revolved around trying to recover. I had stopped socialising because I felt too depressed to take an interest in anything. I just wanted to be on my own.

One or other of my parents stayed with me almost twenty-four hours a day, to ensure that I didn't exercise or vomit. My mother slept in my room to watch me. My thoughts were still focused on trying to exercise and lose weight; if I went for a walk I would start thinking about the calories which I was using up. It was a terrible time. Home was like living on a knife-edge, as my parents could get angry and upset with me, and I could get equally upset with them. I managed to maintain a weight of around seven stone. It was winter, and my body felt freezing.

I had built up some rigid habits about the type of food I would eat, the portion sizes and the timing of meals. My parents encouraged me to become more flexible, and to eat the same food as them, eating three meals a day. They introduced foods which I had been avoiding. After mealtimes we could all feel the tension. I would feel very bloated. I wrote in my diary that I felt like a 'liquefied balloon', and that I 'worried constantly about the next feed'. After eating, I would feel depressed and ashamed, all day and all night.

As I started eating more, and stopped exercising, I went through a period of self-abuse, in which I cut my wrists with razor blades, and burnt myself. It was a sort of justification for eating – I could only allow myself to eat if I then punished myself. I could no longer find a sense of release through exercising or vomiting, and so instead I gained release by harming myself. This was quite serious at the time, although I usually wasn't very aware of what I was doing, as it tended to happen in the times when I felt in deep distress. Afterwards I would feel a lot of guilt.

I became so severely depressed, that I was admitted into a hospital psychiatric ward. Other people on the ward suffered from conditions such as schizophrenia and manic-depression. I found it upsetting to see other young people going through very difficult experiences. Rather than it helping me, I began to pick up unhealthy behaviours and habits from them, and started being even harder on myself. Then after two weeks I discharged myself.

I don't know how I kept going. I had been on a course of self-destruct, but I wanted to come out of it. The choice was either reverting back to excessive exercise and starvation and feeling miserable, or going through this painful process and hoping that it would eventually come to an end.

Very, very slowly it became easier. I became structured in eating three meals a day and snacks. I grew more confident, and gradually started to get better, although on some days all the guilt feelings came back, and when my clothes felt tighter, or I saw that I had gained weight, I found it hard to cope. I was full of fear and anxiety. Part of the fear was that I would no longer be special if I recovered. But then I would come to my senses and think, 'I can start living again now.' I would try to start each morning positively, reminding myself that food was not the be all and end all. Around my seventeenth birthday I thought, 'I've got to get myself out of this now.' I would wake up and think 'This is a fresh start,' and blank off everything that had passed, and aim to recover.

My family were great, especially my parents, who were extremely supportive and understanding. It was a very rough time for them. They went through periods of feeling very guilty. My father felt ashamed because he was my biology teacher and he had taught about anorexia for twenty years, and yet had failed to notice the onset of my symptoms because I had disguised them so well. No one expects it to happen in their family, and when it does, it's easy to miss the signs. My mother gave up her job as a district nurse to look after me. She would talk to me before meals to help me deal with my anxiety about eating. They also accompanied me to appointments with the psychiatrist and the GP. In short, they were there for me when I needed them. Eventually it paid off.

Because my parents were so supportive, I was determined to get well, for their sake. I knew that they were very distressed when I deliberately harmed myself. It nearly brought my mother to a breakdown. The fact that it caused her so much pain actually helped me to stop. Although I felt very tempted to harm myself again, I managed to resist the temptation for the sake of my family. I was left with just the scars. My love for my family, and for God, also gave me the strength to eat at times when I knew I could get away with not eating.

The psychiatrist wanted me to keep a food diary, recording everything which I ate. I found that difficult, because at the end of the day I would look at it and think, 'Gosh, I've eaten all that,' and feel greedy. I had read a lot of books about eating disorders, and these gave me the idea of expanding the food diary. I started to write down my feelings and my progress as well, as I found that more positive. I noted every accomplishment, in what I called my 'victories book'. It was easy for me to focus on what was going badly, and on my failings, and to dismiss my achievements as trivial. When I wrote down my achievements, however, I was able to look back at the end of the day and think, 'Gosh I've done this, and I didn't do that two weeks ago.' The victories might have seemed petty to other people – just an extra mouthful – but they really were triumphs.

My list of victories included such things as making my own breakfast, deciding where to have mid-morning coffee, choosing a sandwich which wasn't 'low calorie', not making a fuss about the size of my dinner, talking to people at church and sitting and watching a film. They all added up. My mother would add comments in my diary at the end of the day, in response to the concerns and achievements which I had described. That gave me the encouragement to go on.

I have a very strong Christian faith. I'm not fanatic, preaching in the streets, but I do have a strong faith in God. I've been a Christian since I was a child, but for a long time that meant little more to me than just trudging along to church on a Sunday. My illness brought out a deeper faith. I had to trust God. When I felt really down, I prayed a lot, and this helped me through. My anorexic thought was, 'You're going to become fat, ugly and miserable' but I knew that I could fight those lies and choose life instead.

I wrote in my thoughts diary:

It is hard sometimes to feel and act normal without any praise because you don't feel 'special' . . . people don't realise how hard you try. What I know is that God sees what I do and it is his love that will conquer everything.

201

I knew that there were better things in life and that I could live for them. I realised that God was there for me, although I couldn't see him, and that he appreciated me for who I was. I didn't have to work, or to be skinny, to gain God's approval. That really was a help through my illness. I wrote in my diary, while I was struggling to recover, 'I could never do this without God and it's his love and words that keep me going day after day. The family also give me a reason to pull out all the stops.'

People at church helped by praying for me, and visiting me so that I didn't feel alone in my battle. They helped me spiritually, even though they didn't know what I was going through mentally.

I kept a daily diary of my prayers and Bible readings. I would read a passage, and write down things from it which would help me during the day. I wrote down verses which jumped out at me, and I wrote my thoughts and prayers. One of the recurring themes was a prayer that God would 'craft me'. I was very doubtful about my physical appearance, and what would happen if I ate – would I become fat? Would I become ugly? What would I become? But I prayed, 'God, just craft me into what you want me to be.' The Bible states that we are like clay, and God is the Potter, who forms us (Isaiah 64:8). I asked God to build me physically as well as spiritually.

For a couple of months, I had appointments with the psychiatrist twice a week. Then we met less frequently, and then we stopped meeting altogether. We spoke about the roots of my illness, such as my low self-esteem. He helped me to realise that anorexia can be overcome, both mentally and physically. He taught me some relaxation techniques, to help me deal with feelings of tension.

Something else which I found helpful was learning to enjoy things again. I found that there were many sources of pleasure in life, even little things which I had always taken for granted, such as being with my family, watching a film, listening to music or going out somewhere. I tried to practise treating myself, instead of punishing myself, although I found this very hard at first. Like eating, it involved giving something to myself, which initially I felt very guilty about. I had to change my whole way of thinking, arguing against the thought that 'I don't deserve this.' I told myself, 'I don't need to starve and punish myself, I can enjoy life.' This was a big change. I began to feel better, and I discovered more things which I could enjoy. My faith helped in this, because I knew that God loved me and had given me good things to enjoy.

I also began to express myself through poetry and art. This was a constructive way to provide a feeling of release, and I used it to replace the destructive methods I had chosen before. I started writing very simple poems, and doodling. I discovered that I liked it, and I had a bit of a talent for it. I did more and more of it.

My weight was slowly increasing. Every time I was weighed and my weight had gone up, I felt anxious. Something in the back of my mind told me that I shouldn't gain weight. I was afraid that I would no longer be special. I was afraid that if I lost the mantle of anorexia, then I wouldn't have anything left – I felt that I was purely 'an anorexic', nothing more. Gradually I tried to accept that I always had been special, and I always would be, whatever the scales said. I wasn't just an anorexic, I was Dan. I had to build up my self-esteem. I learned to take each day as it came and plod on. I still felt some guilt after eating certain foods, but the more I ate them, the easier it became.

It took me about eighteen months of making slow but steady progress before I felt that I had recovered. Now I'm healthy. I weigh about nine stone. I weigh myself now and again, just to make such that my weight is OK; I want to keep on that even keel, but I'm not worried about it. I want to be happy in life. As long as I'm happy and not reverting to the destructive behaviours, and I'm not worried about image or appearance, then it's good. These days, I'm much more interested in jobs and my future than in what I eat or weigh. Food isn't a big issue and there aren't any foods which I won't eat. I have a healthy degree of self-esteem. I've discovered both my good traits and my bad traits, and I have embraced them both. I'm much more confident. I've become a more 'up front' person, and I'm willing to speak my mind – which I would never have done before I became ill. I've really become myself, through recovering from the illness.

I had to be very careful when I was re-introducing exercise into my lifestyle, to ensure that I didn't become obsessive about it again but I don't find it a problem at all now. I'm able to enjoy exercise, but I don't go overboard with it. I just do enough to keep fit and healthy.

As a family, our relationships with each other have become much stronger. We all went through a terrible time when I was ill, but positive things have come out of it. We've reassessed our priorities, and discovered what is important in life.

The love for drawing which developed while I was recovering helped me to win a place at an art school in America. I spent the past year studying there, and I got a lot out of that. I had only just recovered when I went, and at first it felt a bit strange. There was a temptation to relapse into my disordered eating and exercise habits, but I was able to resist the temptation and make healthy choices instead. I had been given a wonderful opportunity, and I wanted to make the most of it, and not flush it down the drain for the sake of losing weight. If anything, my time in America helped me to consolidate my recovery. I was only able to stay there for one year, but I hope to return when I have saved enough money to stand on my own two feet there.

I have discovered that it *is* possible to recover from anorexia. People do go through eating disorders and come out the other side. I believe that I have completely recovered, and I would encourage other people in a similar situation to stick in there, and accept all the help they can. The sooner you can nip this sort of behaviour in the bud, the better. I find it very encouraging to look back and see that I've come through. For me, it was my faith and my supportive family that helped me though and although some people don't have those, they can still overcome the difficulties. They need to find hope in themselves. Even though you might be in the depths of despair and think that life isn't worth living, you should never lose hope. You might even wake tomorrow feeling very different. The struggle will come to an end, even though there are times when it seems that it never will. Some people suddenly reach a turning point and think, 'I'm going to get a pizza and I'm going to recover,' and there's no looking back for them. If that happens that's great. But it's more common for it to be a long, hard, slow battle, as it was in my case. Even with the slow route, gradually you do get there.

Caring for Someone
with an Eating Disorder

14

Robin – A Mother's Story

It all began for us when my daughter Sue came rushing into the house one day, in tears. I was upstairs, and as I looked over the bannister I could see her crying on her father's shoulder. Her first serious boyfriend had ended the relationship, and she was devastated. One of the things she said as she sobbed was, 'I'll never eat again.' Of course, we didn't take a lot of notice of that. But as the weeks passed, we realised that she was losing a lot of weight, and I began to suspect that something was seriously wrong.

Sue was eighteen, and was attending a college course in the afternoons. She generally left the house around three o'clock, shortly before I got home from work, so we used to just miss each other. One afternoon, as I walked into the kitchen after work, I felt uneasy. The kitchen looked too neat and tidy. Teenagers don't leave kitchens like that.

I walked over to the swing bin and lifted the lid. There was the lunch I had left for her, untouched. Feeling concerned, I wandered upstairs to her bedroom. That also seemed too tidy. I'm not sure why, but I looked under her bed. I was stunned by what I saw. There, neatly wrapped in foil and stored in tupperware boxes, were all the evening meals which I had prepared for Sue over the last few weeks.

My initial reaction was sheer panic. I didn't know what to do. I felt sick with fear, because I knew that the thing which had been lurking in the back of my mind, which I hadn't wanted to face up to, was looking like a reality – Sue had anorexia nervosa. She was fascinated by food, storing it in her bedroom, but not allowing herself to eat any of it. Perhaps leaving it in her room was also partly a cry for help, a hope that someone would find it and be able to help her understand her difficulties.

Sadly, at that stage I had little understanding of the problem. When Sue returned home that night, my husband and I confronted her. We tried to make her eat, we tried everything, and we realised that we were losing the battle. We were all getting angry and frustrated. She had made up her mind that she wasn't going to eat, and we couldn't do anything about it.

In the days which followed, we talked to Sue for hours. She was severely depressed. I can remember her sitting in our bedroom at about two o'clock one morning. She was in a foetal position leaning against the radiator, and she told us, 'I just want to go over to that corner and fade away.' That's exactly what she was trying to do, she was trying to fade away.

It was a very strange situation. We had been living ordinary lives, then suddenly everything had changed; suddenly our daughter was deliberately starving herself to death in front of us. We felt completely helpless. We couldn't make her eat, she would only have brought it all back up, so it was pointless.

As we didn't get anywhere struggling with Sue on our own, I took her to the doctor. He admitted he didn't know much about eating disorders, so he just weighed her (which upset her), told her to eat more, and referred us to a psychiatrist. Initially we made an appointment privately, so that we would be seen quickly. The psychiatrist phoned me three times before the first session to make sure that I would bring the money with me. The first two times I thought it was unusual. When he called me half an hour before I was due to leave for the appointment, again to make sure that I would bring the money, I decided to cancel the appointment. I didn't want to entrust my daughter's life to someone who only cared about money.

So we went back to the doctor, who arranged for us to see

another psychiatrist. Sue met with him once a month for a while, which may have helped her in some respects, although she continued to lose weight.

In order to increase my own understanding, I began to read all the books I could find on eating disorders. Many of the books seemed to suggest that eating disorders stem from problems in the family. To see my daughter fading away before my eyes was very hard, but to think that I might have been part of the cause of the problem was harder still.

Although it was difficult, these books did help me to think honestly about our family and about myself. I realised that as parents we had been very dominant and over-protective. We had tried so hard to protect Sue from disappointments, that we had not really let her develop the skills of coping with difficulties on her own. When the big let-down had come, the break-up with her boyfriend, she did not know how to cope with her disappointment. We thought that we were doing the right thing in protecting her, but we hadn't allowed her to go through the hurts and the traumas that teenagers do go through. We had shielded her too much from these things.

As I considered our family dynamics, and read the books, the second thing which I realised was that we did not express feelings healthily. All negative feelings tended to be suppressed, including feelings of rejection, hurt, loneliness and anger. This pattern had developed without us noticing.

The third thing I observed was that we had communication problems. My husband and I did not really listen to our three children, or consider them as people in their own right. In particular, my husband did not allow the children to disagree with him.

A friend pointed out to me a fourth characteristic of our family. One day I complained to her on the phone, 'Sue is so dramatic, we have such terrible scenes, it's so difficult to cope with.' My friend replied, 'Yes, but you're dramatic too – in fact, all your family are rather dramatic you know.' I was very polite to her as I put the phone down, but inside I felt furious. I marched into the next room and protested, 'How *dare* she say that I'm dramatic,' flinging my arms around and looking rather – dramatic! I suddenly realised that she was right, I was over-dramatic. I hadn't seen it in myself before.

As a result of reading books and beginning to look at myself, our family, and how we handled things, I began to become more self-aware. The amazing thing to me now is that I was thirty-nine at the time and I'd never given a thought as to why I reacted or behaved in the way that I did. At the time I felt extremely guilty, blaming myself for Sue's illness. I played over in my mind every time that I had smacked her, and I thought – did I smack her too early, or too often? When I couldn't bear blaming myself any more, I started to blame my husband instead – maybe he had been too strict, or too busy. We both felt a need to lay the blame somewhere, and we blamed each other. This caused a great strain on our marriage; the stress was driving us apart. There were times when he and I were at church on Sunday, and before taking Communion we had to reach out to each other, hold hands and say, 'I'm sorry.'

I used to visualise myself taking my load of guilt to Jesus, and putting it down at the foot of cross. I would feel tremendous relief. But after a few days had passed I would find that I had picked up the guilt again bit by bit, and was once again bowed under the weight of it. I had to take it back to the cross again, and again, and again, until I learned to leave it there, and to receive God's forgiveness. I honestly don't think I could have coped with the guilt if I hadn't been a Christian. I allowed God to take this burden from me, and slowly I came to a place where I had peace about it.

Sue was still going to college at this time. It's difficult to understand how she managed to continue there when she was so weak. I think that it was a good thing that she did keep going, because the last thing she needed was to have an empty, lonely life. She needed to be with people.

She always insisted on walking to college, even though my husband drove our second daughter to the same college. He would stop the car when he passed Sue, but she always refused to accept a lift. He felt devastated driving on, leaving his frail daughter struggling alone in the wind and the snow.

I continued to search for any help I could find for Sue and for myself. There weren't any self-help groups available at that time in our area, but somebody told me about one in another town. I phoned the number, and talked to a young woman who had been bulimic and had recovered. As I spoke to her, even in all my anxiety I sensed something was wrong. I asked how she had got over the eating disorder, and she said she was helped by a spiritualist lady. I felt too tired to discuss it and was going to put the phone down, but I felt I had to say to her, 'I don't agree with spiritualism, I'm a born-again Christian.' She replied, 'But they helped me, I lost two babies through bulimia and those ladies helped me get over it.' She asked if I would accept some leaflets about eating disorders, and I replied, 'Yes, but would you accept some leaflets about how to become a born-again Christian?' She said she would and so I wrote to her, but we didn't go to the group.

We were trying all the avenues we could think of, but I wasn't finding any help which I felt happy with as a caring mother and a Christian. Sue's health was deteriorating rapidly. I had to help her up the stairs, and I had to put her into bed. She was about five foot ten, and she weighed just five and a half stone. She was very, very ill. She was given the option of going into hospital, but I wanted her at home. I don't know if that was right or not.

I cried out to God, asking him, 'Why?' Why was God letting this happen to us? I couldn't understand it.

Before Sue became ill, I had thought that I was quite a strong Christian, as I was always helping other people but when Sue became ill, I found that I could no longer pray. I felt that I was hanging on to God by my fingertips. I remember saying once, 'Lord, I don't know if you love me, I don't know if you're going to heal Sue, I don't know if you care about me, I don't know if you're even looking at me at this time, all I know this minute is that you are alive, you are real.' I realised afterwards that I'd echoed words spoken by Job when he was suffering, 'I know that my Redeemer lives' (Job 19:25). I had no doubt whatsoever that God existed, because I had seen many miracles in other people's lives, and I had known God working powerfully in my own life. I knew that God was real, but I didn't know what he was going to do in this situation. I was in total panic because my daughter looked as if she was going to die. I could tell by the faces of those around me that *they* thought she was going to die too. I wasn't able to help her, because I was only just coping myself. All I was doing to her was adding to her own fear, because she could see the fear in me.

I wasn't feeling God's presence at this time, but just like the psalmist in Psalm 77, I made myself remember the times in the past when I had felt God's presence. This helped to build up my faith, and I knew that one day I would experience that wonderful presence again. I decided that I had to surrender to God and trust him, and believe that he could make a path through the Red Sea for me to travel on, even if I couldn't see any sign of it.

Around this time, some Christian friends travelled quite a distance to visit us. They arrived, had dinner with us, and then they suddenly said to me, 'We feel the Lord wants us to pray for you.' I was taken aback, and asked, '*Me?* It's Sue who needs the prayers, it's Sue who needs the help.' I was so unaware of my own needs that my way of coping was to ignore them. My friends bravely continued, 'We've always felt that you're very anxious.' I protested, 'No, no, no, I'm not an anxious person, not at all.' But they weren't put off, and explained, 'We feel the Lord has led us to pray for you about this anxiety, to set you free from it.' They opened their Bible at Philippians 4:6, and read, 'Do not be anxious about anything, but in everything, by prayer and petition, with thanksgiving, present your requests to God.' Very unwillingly, I let them lay hands on me and pray for me. As they did so, it was as if a lovely warm, comforting blanket was wrapped around my head and my body. I wanted to say something or do something, but I couldn't move. The Lord spoke to me during that time of peace and tranquillity. I felt that he said to me, 'You're always trying to do things to please me, but you don't have to please me, my love for you is totally and utterly unconditional.' I don't know how long I sat under that warm blanket of God's love, but it felt like a long, long time. That was the first time that I truly believed that the Lord really did love and accept me. This was a major turning point in my life, as I realised that I did not have to prove anything to God, I didn't even have to move, because he loved me as I was.

This didn't stop me feeling distressed about Sue's illness. Another friend noticed my struggle, and spoke to me about a passage in Genesis 21. Here it says that Hagar wept as she knew that her son was dying in the desert because there was no food or water. I could identify with that. I was weeping too, as I felt that I was watching my daughter die. She looked so ill, and she seemed very determined that she was not going to eat. The passage continues, 'Then God opened her eyes and she saw a well of water. So she went and filled the skin with water and gave the boy a drink' (Genesis 21:19).

My friend said that, just as God had shown Hagar a well where she could be refreshed, so he could show me a place of refreshment. One of my concerns at the time was that we attended a very small church, and there wasn't anyone there who seemed able to help us. People said, 'We'll pray for you,' but no one knew how to help, and I felt totally and utterly alone. I longed for a church where we could receive the support we badly needed. My friend said that, like Hagar, I had been too full of fear to see the well. The well had been there all the time, but Hagar hadn't been able to see it until God opened her eyes to it. My friend encouraged me, 'Somewhere nearby there's a church where you can go and get spiritual food and drink, and you can bring it back to Sue and help her.'

As she left me that day, she asked, 'Do you know that Sue isn't going to die from anorexia?' I replied, 'No I don't.' She continued, 'Well, I do. God's shown me that she isn't going to die from it.' I felt that wasn't enough for me. If it was true, I wanted God to give *me* that assurance too. When she'd gone, I prayed, 'Lord, I need to know, will you just show me that she's not going to die from this illness – then I feel I'll be able to be stronger.'

I was very depressed at this time, and I must admit that while my friend was talking about Hagar, I didn't show much interest. She must have been disappointed. After she left I thought to myself, 'She came all this way to bring this word to me, the least I can do is to read it again.' I began to read the passage, and I realised that this was the living word of God, sharper than a double-edged sword. I had been so full of fear that I couldn't hear God – my heart was sort of muffled-up. But this sharp sword began to penetrate into my heart.

As I went to bed that night I prayed again, 'Please, Lord, just show me that my daughter isn't going to die.' In the morning when I woke up, I turned to the Bible passage which had been selected for that day in the Bible study notes which I used. It was Psalm 107. About halfway through the words sprang out at me: 'Some became fools through their rebellious ways . . . they loathed all food and drew near the gates of death. Then they cried to the LORD in their trouble . . . He sent forth his word and healed them; he rescued them from the grave' (Psalm 107:17–20). I believed that God was speaking to my heart, and tremendous peace and strength poured into me. I knew that Sue wasn't about to die. I clung on to that hope.

That gave me strength in the days ahead. I thought, 'Lord, you are in control, you haven't let me go, you've allowed this to happen to my family, for some reason.' As I began to come before God, I knew it wasn't going to be a quick healing, because God was going to change us through it.

Soon after this we did find another church. The people there didn't particularly understand eating disorders, but they prayed for us, and listened to us. One Sunday the pastor told me, 'The Lord keeps waking me up in the middle of the night to pray for Sue.' I replied, 'Well, she's awake every night and so are we, listening to her prowling around the house.' He promised to continue praying for her. A couple of weeks later he said the Lord was waking his wife up as well and they were both praying for her in the middle of the night. I replied, 'Keep praying please, because she's still awake nearly all night, and we're so tired.' Several weeks went by, and then one Sunday morning he told me they were still waking in the middle of the night, and they had started to thank God for what he had already done for Sue, and for what he was doing for her. From that time on she began to sleep all night. I was so thankful for people who kept praying when I felt unable to.

Some people avoided me because they didn't know what to say, or because they felt embarrassed, or were as worried as I was. Others only talked to me about Sue's problems. I didn't always want to talk about anorexia, because I lived and breathed that. What I appreciated was people who came and chatted about anything else. I needed to be reminded that there was still a normal world outside our house. Sometimes I was invited for a meal, although not many people gave that sort of invitation because people felt awkward about feeding me, given the nature of Sue's problems. When it did happen, I felt thrilled that I was doing something normal, and being considered as a person in my own right, and not just as the mother of an anorexic. It was a great relief when I was able to spend time relaxing with friends away from our home.

There were times when I appreciated people who listened and just let me talk. Until this point I had been the type of person who didn't talk about problems. I had always pretended that everything was fine. I'd been like that ever since I was young, and when I became a Christian it intensified because I thought, 'I'm a Christian now, so everything's got to be good.' I worked hard at giving the appearance that everything was OK. All of a sudden I couldn't keep it up, because I was breaking up inside. Anorexia was the most terrible thing that ever happened to us as a family, and yet it was also the most wonderful thing, because it made us show our feelings. It made me let go of my pretence.

My brother and sister-in-law were a great help to me. I started to go round to their house and talk for hours. The pressure had become so great, that I thought I'd burst if I didn't tell someone. I poured out my heart to my brother, and shared the truth about how I really felt. Before this, he had always seen me as the strong one, the one who helped him out, and he had felt inadequate. Suddenly our roles were reversed, and there was I, needing him. One night I broke down, and wept. He put his arms around me, and promised to help me. As I cried, I could literally feel the tension draining out of me because I wasn't pretending any more. It was like being set free. My brother told me afterwards that showing him that I needed him meant more to him than anything I had ever done before.

Unfortunately for Sue, the young people at our new church were slightly afraid of her, as they had not known her before her illness, and her behaviour was strange at times. She did not allow them to get close to her, and she did not have any friends at college either. She spent a lot of time alone. A couple from the church came to the rescue, by inviting her around for an evening at least once a week. Afterwards they often found food hidden all over their house, even in their plant pots. Later, when Sue began to binge-eat, food would disappear from their fridge. People who put up with that are good friends! I used to look forward to the break from anxiety when Sue was at their house, because I knew they were going to pick her up at the door, take her to their home and look after her for an evening.

There was tremendous tension in our home most of the time, and having Sue invited out helped a great deal.

As well as my Christian faith and friends within the church, something else that helped me was realising that my behaviour within my marriage and family was learned behaviour. That is, my childhood (including experiences which I had no control over) had definitely had an effect on me and the way I behaved. I came to realise that we all make mistakes as parents, and it made little sense for me to condemn myself for not being a perfect parent. As I thought and prayed, I began to understand a bit more about myself, and why I acted the way I did.

I had felt unwanted for as long as I could remember. As a young girl, my mother more or less rejected me. I was the third girl in the family, and she had wanted a son. Before I was born, she had given birth to a boy who had died. I looked like him, so my parents gave me the same name, Robin. I must have been a constant painful reminder to my mother of the son she had lost. When I was four, she finally had the son that she had longed for, my younger brother. I grew up believing that she loved him more than she loved me.

My father died when I was thirteen. He had been ill for two years before this, and although everyone in the family had known that he was going to die, no one spoke about it. It was like a bad atmosphere that was always there. When dad died neither my brother nor I were allowed to go to the funeral. That was quite common in those days. I didn't really get over my father's death, because I wasn't allowed to grieve.

I learned various ways to suppress my feelings, just as my mother had done. I found out from my older sister that my mother had suffered a nervous breakdown, and a doctor had suggested that having another baby might help her get over it. I was that baby, born to help my mother avoid her feelings. Like my mother, I thought that having babies might help me cope with life. As a young girl, I used to think to myself, 'When I'm grown up, I'm going to have lots of children, and they will love me.' Instead of wanting children so I could love them, I wanted them so they would love me.

My mother remarried when I was sixteen. The first I knew about it was overhearing her talking about it with her future husband. My brother and I were not invited to the wedding. My mother didn't really communicate with us; I don't think she knew how to.

When I was seventeen, I found her one night in the kitchen attempting to commit suicide by gassing herself. It was the middle of the night, and it felt like a terrible nightmare. My stepfather rushed out of the house with a packed suitcase and my brother and I managed to get my mother back into bed, but we were very upset. I tried to stay awake all night because I thought she might try again; eventually I fell asleep in the early hours of the morning. A few hours later, I woke up to the smell of bacon and eggs cooking. I went downstairs looking absolutely wrecked. There was my stepfather sitting reading the paper, eating breakfast, as if nothing had happened. My mother was at the stove and she said, 'Hurry up, you'll be late for work.' Astonished, I replied, 'I can't go to work.' She firmly retorted, 'Why ever not?' I knew that was her way of saying, 'Don't you ever speak about this again.' And we never did.

This is just one example of the suppression of feelings and lack of communication within my own family as I grew up. As I allowed myself to think about these experiences, I began to see that I had passed a lot of these patterns onto my children, without realising it. Sue couldn't shout and scream about how she felt, as that was not the done thing in our family. I think starvation was her way of showing the family, 'I'm hurting, I'm angry and I don't know how to express it.' I began to ask myself how I could help her to discover her own identity and allow herself to express emotions instead of numbing them away by starving.

I didn't want Sue to repeat the difficulties I'd had when I was her age. When I was eighteen, I had left home, a very insecure, immature young girl. Maybe if I'd spent that time on my own, or sharing a flat with a friend, I could have had the chance to mature. Instead, I ran away to my husband, who was a very strong character. Because I had very low self-esteem, I was happy for him to take control of my life. I hadn't really discovered my own identity.

I had my first baby when I was twenty-one, and that was Sue. My husband had been an only child, and was used to getting a lot of attention. He seemed jealous about the amount of time I spent with the baby. Moreover, I had moved away from my mother, my sisters and my brother, and my husband didn't really like me to see much of them. We didn't speak about our difficulties, but there was a feeling of tension all the time. I struggled a lot with this first child, and I was very anxious about her. I didn't know how to mother her, because I hadn't been mothered. I had never been held on my mother's knee, I'd never been told that I was loved, and I didn't know how to express love for my child. I was a child trying to be a mother.

Two years later I had another daughter, and life improved. It improved financially and I seemed to learn to cope with life better, and from the outside we must have looked pretty good. We had a nice house, I had a nice husband, two lovely little girls, and all my efforts began to go into the family and the home. My husband began to throw himself more and more into his work.

We both had deep emotional needs that had never been met, and we were using various methods to cope with life and to repress these needs. We tried to fill our lives with other things. I turned to alcohol to give me the confidence I lacked. I wasn't an alcoholic, but I had to have a couple of drinks before I went out to any business dinner. I would also have quite a few drinks while I was out.

My past had affected me in a much deeper way than I had realised. It affected the way I behaved in relationships, the way I communicated and the way I coped with emotions and with life. It was at this time that I became a born-again Christian, and God did a lot of healing in me. And I thought that was it. I didn't realise just how much more healing was needed.

Not long after this, my husband also became a Christian. We moved to a new part of the country, and I had a third baby. Sue found it difficult to cope with all the changes in our family life. She was twelve years old, and was showing signs of not wanting to grow up. She didn't like the way her body was developing, and she used to cry about it in the bath. I didn't realise how serious this was. I didn't meet her emotional needs at that time, as I was too involved with the baby and moving, and I was wrapped up in myself. My husband was excited about having become a Christian, and he had a demanding new job, so he didn't have much time for Sue either. About six months after we moved, I started to notice problems. Until then Sue had been an easy girl, mainly because she had learned to suppress all her feelings. She had seen the way her mother and father behaved and I suppose she didn't know any other way to live. When I look back, I think that God wasn't satisfied with this, he was about to rip the whole thing open.

Sue couldn't bear it when she started having periods, as it was a sign of womanhood. She had a nervous breakdown, although I didn't realise at the time that was what it was. The doctor prescribed tranquillizers for her. I didn't even realise they were tranquillizers until watching a TV show one night, Sue said, 'Those are the tablets I'm on.' I was shocked. She was about thirteen then. She began a terrible struggle to come off them, but she had a lot of willpower, and did manage it. She had some sort of recovery from that breakdown, and she became a Christian around that time. I was very happy that she had apparently recovered. I just wanted the whole problem to go away and never come back. Unfortunately, the underlying problems were still there.

Sue must have suffered a great deal in the years which followed. She wasn't able to tell us how she felt, because she sensed that I didn't want to face this sort of problem. We didn't face up to why Sue had suffered from a breakdown. It was all too painful and we just wanted to carry on as normal. But when Sue was eighteen years old she became anorexic.

By this time we had moved again, and Sue had been going out with a Christian young man for about a year. She was very serious about him. When he finished the relationship, she couldn't cope with the rejection and the emotions which she felt.

As she starved, she became obsessed with food. The obsession kept her mind off all the underlying problems. If her mind was constantly on food, she didn't have to experience the pain of rejection. I decided not to force her to eat and to stop fussing about it. This was challenged after a while by a psychiatric nurse who was a friend of my husband. She told me that I should monitor everything that Sue ate, and that I should weigh her every day. After thinking about it, I came to the conclusion that the food issue was like a great big red herring thrown out to put us off the scent. We needed to get to what was underneath it all. So I didn't monitor Sue's food. Instead, I encouraged her to talk. We talked for hours on end.

Later I found a poem which Sue had written in the front of a Bible while she was anorexic:

Please welcome this lump of dejection, that is me, Father
I can't lift up my head
I can't start to look for you
But please take me as I am
And help me through the dark.
I can't offer you energy or enthusiasm.
I can't offer you love or worship
I can only offer me,
Drawn in, and hurting.
Please hold me gently, Lord.

She copied that from somewhere and we don't know who wrote it, but it describes exactly how she felt at the time.

A lot of feelings of guilt surfaced from one or two things Sue had done in the past, ordinary things that many adolescents go through. Sue had never felt able to talk about these things and had carried unnecessary guilt around for years. I encouraged her to express her feelings openly.

I also encouraged her to go out and mix with other people as much as possible. At first she didn't want to do this. She had isolated herself from her friends, and she spent a lot of time in her room. She had begun to cling to me, and initially I was pleased about her dependence on me. Because I had felt unloved for much of my life, I was delighted that I had such a close, loving relationship with my daughter. I used to think of my children as an extension of me. This was especially the case with Sue, as she was the eldest. She was very tall and mature for her age, and I tended to treat her like an adult, because she seemed so grown up. I thought that it was really good that we were like friends. But it wasn't good. She needed me to be a mother she could rely on, not a friend. Because I desperately wanted my children to love me, I overwhelmed them and unwittingly tried to control them, so that they would need me. Sue needed to become independent from me, and make friends with people her own age. I realised that I should let go of her emotionally.

'Letting go' might sound easy, but it was an extremely painful thing for me to do, especially because Sue was still very ill. Her friends from college sometimes asked her to go out with them, and she always refused. She found it difficult to relate to people of her own age; she depended on me instead, for all of her support and friendship. During her illness she had grown closer to me than ever, and it was incredibly hard to step back from her. I realised that as long as I was there she wasn't going to take the opportunity of spending time with friends. Up until this point I had gone out to the cinema with her, to try to engage her in normal activities. Now I told her I wouldn't go out with her anymore, as I wanted her to go with her friends instead. For a time, she didn't go out at all, but I did not give in and after a while she began to get so desperate that she went out with her friends again, just occasionally to begin with. It must have been very hard for her, and I felt proud of her.

A number of mothers of anorexic daughters have told me that they put on weight when their daughters were ill, in an attempt to get their daughter to eat. We went through that phase too. At one point, Sue would only eat if I was eating as well. If she appeared and asked me, 'Have you eaten? What are you having?', even if I'd already eaten, I would have another meal in the hope that this would encourage her to eat too. This didn't always work. Often I would eat and she would leave her food.

Sue was very fussy about what she ate. She only ate very specific foods, at specific times. For a while she would only eat a salad roll. At another point she would eat one wholemeal muffin. She wouldn't touch it, I had to prepare it in a certain way and then give it to her. It had to be sliced twice, which was hard to do. I got very good at it! At another stage all she would eat was a particular type of cheese croissant. If the first shop I tried hadn't got any of the right type, I would go to the next shop, and if they had sold out, I would go to the next one. I would try every shop in the town, and if none of the shops had any, I would go to the next town. We would run anywhere and do anything if we thought it would make Sue eat. I thought that was the only way to help her get well. Now I realise that wasn't the answer, as by letting her manipulate us all, we helped maintain the disordered eating. Anorexia and bulimia can be manipulative of the family, but only because the sufferer is crying out for help because she doesn't know what else to do. I learned to offer Sue help in other ways, but to stop allowing her to use food to control the family. I stopped eating extra meals to please her, and I put the onus on her, so that she had to sort her own food out. I tried to become less protective of her, and to let her control her own life.

Letting go meant being determined not to give in to Sue's every whim. It meant allowing her to make her own mistakes, to fall flat on her face sometimes, to be buffeted about by the world and to learn how to survive and come through stronger. It meant letting her become her own person, even if she disagreed with me and chose a lifestyle which I didn't approve of. Letting go didn't mean turning my back on her or becoming cold and indifferent; it meant loving with no strings attached.

One day Sue agreed to help at a lunch club for elderly people, and I felt thrilled, thinking she had turned a corner and was willing to mix with people, instead of hiding away. The pastor's wife had invited Sue to help, thinking that at least she would be with people, and maybe she would eat something. When Sue got back home afterwards I asked her if she had eaten lunch there, and she said, 'Oh yes.' She described the meal and said how nice it was. That night I went to a prayer meeting, wanting to thank God for this encouragement. The pastor's wife met me at the meeting, with the words, 'Sue really did enjoy the lunch club, but what a pity that she wouldn't eat.' I felt devastated. I cried all the way back from the meeting, because my hopes seemed to be built up and then dashed, built up and then dashed again. Life seemed full of disappointments. However, many people were praying for Sue, and often I would feel the power of their prayers sustaining me.

I was still reading a lot of books about eating disorders, and I was changing. I was becoming more open, and learning to assert myself in my marriage and my other relationships. I was also learning to let go of Sue and allow her to become her own person. I saw signs of improvement in her condition. But this improvement was followed by a time when nothing seemed to change at all. I found that the hardest time of all.

I read in Ephesians 6:13, 'Put on the full armour of God, so that . . . you may be able to stand your ground, and after you have done everything, to stand.' I felt that God was saying to me, 'You've done everything you can. You've been open to me, you've allowed me to begin to change you, you've allowed me to heal you in many ways, you've stopped pretending, you've prayed for your daughter, you've shown her unconditional love, you've supported her. You've done everything you can, and now you must stand in that, and believe that I'm going to complete the work.'

I knew that I had prayed, tried everything the books suggested and done all I could. Having done everything, I just had to 'stand', and trust in God. I realised that faith is when we can't see anything happening but we still trust, and that was what I had to do. I had to say, 'I'm not going to strive, I'm not going to wear myself out, I'm going to wait and believe that God will bring us all through this.'

Eventually, there were signs of further improvement. Sue began to go out with friends more often, and she started to let go of some of her anorexic behaviours. But in their place she adopted new bulimic patterns. She would eat huge quantities of food, and then make herself sick. Like the anorexia, this was also a cry for help and an expression of negative feelings, but the control had gone. I encouraged Sue to talk about her binge-eating. Why did she think she did it, what led up to it, and how did she feel leading up to the binge and during the binge? We identified foods which seemed to trigger her binge – chocolate, dried fruit and icing sugar. I stopped buying them. If she wanted to buy them then that was up to her, but I could manage without them. Sue learned that bingeing was not failing, but it was a way of coping. She found it very hard to fail, and I tried to teach her that it's better to try and fail than not to try at all. We began to learn ways of relaxing without the involvement of food. I praised her when she managed to resist the urge to binge and go and see a friend instead. I knew that took strength, because the feelings that she got when she wanted to binge were very powerful.

Some time after Sue had started binge-eating, the pastor at my church told me about a girl who had recovered from anorexia, who he thought would be able to help us. I spoke with her, and she told me that she had been anorexic, and some people had prayed with her and she'd been totally healed. I replied, 'I'm ever so sorry, I'm not being rude, but you can't help me, because I'm going through it.' Although I was pleased to hear about people who had recovered quickly, I felt that they could not identify with the long, slow battle which we were fighting every day. I found Sue's bulimia even harder to cope with than the anorexia, but I still believed that she wasn't going to die from it. I believed that we were going to come through it, and that we were going to become stronger people.

Sue had been anorexic for about eighteen months, and she then struggled with bulimia for three years. Her mood swings were terrible to live with. She was mixing more, but at home her behaviour was very hard to cope with.

At this time my mother-in-law became very ill. I found her one day collapsed on the floor. We discovered that she had cancer, and she came to live with us for a while, but she was coming towards the end of her life, and after a few months she was moved into a hospice where she could receive the medical attention she needed. My husband used to stay with her all night, and I stayed with her all day. It was a time of terrible stress, as we watched her suffering.

It was December, but because I was spending so much time at the hospice, I hadn't prepared much for Christmas but one thing I had done was to buy a Christmas cake. I used to put all the Christmas things on top of my wardrobe, and I had put the cake there. One day when I went to put some presents there too, I discovered that the cake had gone. Sue had eaten it – the whole, large Christmas cake which had been intended for our family celebration. I found little daily hassles like this very draining. I was trying hard to prepare for Christmas, and there was nothing to show for it. Sue hadn't even told me what she had done. At times like this I felt furious with her, and the way her illness was affecting the family, and leaving me so exhausted. At one point I even hit her. It wasn't the right thing to do, but living with someone who has an eating disorder can drive you to the end of your resources. I decided that I needed to be firm with Sue. We had to think about the others in the family, and start laying down some rules. The rules seemed to help her to improve.

I kept trying to encourage Sue to give up the disordered eating patterns, because they had become a habit, a way of life. I realised that if she didn't replace the eating disorder with something else she was just going to be left with an empty gap, which is the last thing a person with bulimia needs. I knew that I had to encourage her to take hold of something else before she could let go of the bulimia. If someone has a crutch and you snatch it away, they will fall over. But if you reach out a steadying hand, and you walk with them, then gradually remove the hand, they may manage to walk alone. I saw myself as offering Sue a hand until she was able to walk by herself. I hoped that she could replace the eating disorder with friendships, to fill the emptiness inside her.

She started going to see a counsellor, through the charity MIND. I could have taken her by car, dropped her off outside the door, waited for her for an hour and brought her home. But I realised that she had to want to get well herself, rather than because I forced her to. So I gave her money to go by train to the appointments. Sometimes she got there, and sometimes she spent the money on food instead. She had to learn that if she spent the money on food she didn't get the counselling. I kept giving her the money, and a lot of the time she did get to the sessions, and found them helpful.

By this time she had left college, and had stopped going to church. She got a job behind a bar, one or two evenings a week. This was not the lifestyle which I would have chosen for her, but like the father in the parable of the prodigal son, I had to let her make her own decisions. I was challenged when I thought about my motives, in the past, for putting pressure on Sue to be a Christian. A major reason for doing this was my concern about what people in the church would think of me. It took a long time for me to get to the point when I really didn't care about what any person thought, I just cared about what God thought.

I hadn't put pressure on my children to achieve well at school, but I did put pressure on them morally. When I became a Christian, I taught my children that they had to start living as Christians. As they became old enough to decide for themselves, I found it difficult to allow them to have free will. It was as if I was holding Sue up to God and saying, 'Lord, here you are,' but I was still gripping onto her. God wanted me to trust him to look after Sue. When we release our children, we don't release them to nothingness, we release them to the Lord. We do this in the knowledge that God is in control and hears our prayers.

The bar job suited Sue, because she was socialising, but she also had a barrier of a bar between her and other people, and this helped her feel safe. At last she was doing what she wanted to do. She also got a day-time job as a hotel receptionist. Again she was mixing with people but had a desk between her and them. She started to make new friends. She felt like the odd one out, and at the back of her mind she always worried, 'They won't accept me if they know what I'm really like.' Nevertheless, she did gradually begin to trust a few people, and she allowed them to get to know her better. In particular, she made friends with two sisters, who accepted her, warts and all. On many occasions she arranged to pick them up to go out somewhere, but then she didn't turn up. Her friends would phone, and I would find Sue lying on her bed with a hot water bottle on her stomach, having binged because she was panicking about going out. It must have been very difficult for her, but little by little she made progress. Although there were many set-backs, she gradually started to mix with people, and to let go of the bulimia.

Sue began to have the courage to stop making herself sick after eating. Unfortunately, that did not mean that she had completely recovered from her eating problems. She went through a stage of compulsively overeating, which I feel was part of her recovery. She still seemed unable to control her eating, and she used food for comfort. Although putting on weight upset her on one level, on another level it helped her feel safe. Like the table at the bar, the extra weight was a barrier between her and other people. Since being rejected by her boyfriend when she was eighteen, she had grown terrified of repeating the experience, and so she was afraid of having relationships with boys. As she gained weight, she felt safer, thinking that men would not find her attractive.

This stage of compulsive eating lasted for about six months, and it took a further two years before her eating patterns really returned to normal. During this time she continued to mix with friends, and to discover that they accepted her whatever her weight was. Gradually she began to lose her fear of men, as she mixed with them both at work and in the group of friends she socialised with. She also began to relax and to discover and accept herself. As she did so, she had less need to use food to make her feel better, or extra weight to help her feel safe. She learned other ways of coping with life. She started eating more normally, and her weight fell to a normal level. She found a boyfriend whom she was happy with. She gave up dieting, because as soon as she told herself she must not eat chocolate, chips or any other type of food, she immediately started craving for that forbidden substance, and was likely to binge. So she started to allow herself moderate amounts of these foods. That satisfied her.

The journey wasn't smooth – there were struggles and set-backs. She had to make all the changes herself. All we could do was offer encouragement and listen to her. In the early stages of her recovery, if she told me that she was feeling upset or fearful, I would feel terrible. Later I learned to let her unload her feelings without being dragged down myself. She wanted me to listen to her, not to provide all the answers. Once I understood this, I just let her unburden on me, and then I let go of it.

During her recovery, Sue had to learn to listen to her own body. She had grown so used to ignoring pain and ignoring her own needs that she didn't even know when she was ill. She had to learn to recognise when she was hungry and when she felt full, as she had overridden these signals for a long time. It took many months before she learned to care for herself again.

In the past Sue had let people make unreasonable demands on her. Part of caring for herself was learning that she did not have to do everything which other people wanted her to do. She became more assertive. The painful thing for me was realising that she didn't have to do everything I wanted her to do, either. She decided that she wanted to move to Manchester. I complained that Manchester was too far away, and I didn't know the way there, and I hated leaving the motorway near there! I was surprised by my own feelings – I thought I had let go of her, but I was extremely upset that she wanted to move away. I worried that she would not survive without me. I thought she needed to see me at least once a week, but she didn't. She was an adult, she was well again, and what she really needed was the opportunity to be responsible for herself. She moved, and it was good for both of us.

As Sue began to take up less of my attention, I had more time to notice my other two children. I realised, with horror, just how much they had been suffering. Our whole family had been controlled by Sue's eating disorder. When she first started suffering from anorexia, her sisters were aged sixteen and six. Ruth, the sixteen-year-old, was attending the same college as Sue. Sue looked so emaciated that Ruth felt embarrassed to be associated with her, and she used to ignore her. If Sue waved at Ruth, and Ruth's friends asked 'Who's that?' Ruth would deny even knowing her. Ruth later felt extremely guilty about this, wishing that she had helped Sue. It took years for her to realise that there was little that she could have done to help, and that she had coped in the only way she knew how, by pretending the problem did not exist. She expressed this in a poem which she wrote:

Dear Sister,
I do love you, but I don't know how to handle your ways,
and your appearance.
I want to hug you and say 'everything is going to be alright'
But I can't bring myself to touch you.
I feel hatred towards you
But it's not you I hate, it's the illness that you have.
I wish that I could help
But I feel so helpless.
And so I will just pretend
That you don't exist.

My six-year-old daughter Jill also felt very worried and confused. No one sat down with her and explained what was the matter with her big sister. We assumed that she was too young to notice. She sensed that something was very, very wrong, but she did not know quite what it was, which was even more confusing and worrying for her. She was certainly more aware of the problem than I had realised. When she was about eight, she saw an emaciated girl, and she commented, 'Look, that girl's anorexic.' That was the first time I realised that she was aware of anorexia. She had been trying to make sense of the situation for two years by then.

Both Ruth and Jill at times felt frustrated, frightened and angry, because their older sister was getting all our attention. Then they would feel guilty for wanting attention when Sue looked so ill. If we had communicated well with each other, we could have talked about and dealt with these feelings at the time. I wish that we had sat down together and answered their questions. Instead, we had made the eating disorder an unmentionable subject, so it was only much later that these issues were resolved.

I realise now that when someone has an eating disorder, the whole family needs support, and benefits from an explanation of what is happening. The mood swings and manipulation which occur mean that the whole family is affected. Sisters and brothers need someone to come alongside them and be interested in them, not just in the person who is ill. They need somebody to listen to how they are getting on, and to give them attention. I am thankful to God that Ruth and Jill managed to come through the experience, and that I am able to have a good relationship with each of them now.

Nowadays, Sue says she is determined to make up for the years of her life which she missed out on. When she was ill for all those years, I often wondered whether we would ever be able to have a normal relationship again. Thankfully, we now have a very good relationship. We are not dependent on each other. We love each other with the kind of love that sets the other free to be themselves. I no longer put conditions on my love for her, or for any of my children. I just love them for the people that they are.

My mother had terrible problems in her family, and her mother did as well. I'm determined to try not to pass these problems on to the next generation. Ruth has now got two little girls, and she has said to me, 'The things I've learned from Sue having anorexia are amazing.' She has learned not to hold too tightly to her children. Her eldest child is only four, but she is already learning to be her own person. Ruth said to me, 'I don't think I'd have done that if we hadn't been through what we've been through.' I believe God has stopped the cycle of problems which was trapping our family.

I think that one of the most important gifts which I have given my children, is the example I have set them by completely changing how I live. I used to be a weak, fearful, anxious woman. Through becoming more self-aware, I have changed considerably. I have become more assertive. I have learned to express my emotions. Lots of suppressed feelings came tumbling out of my aching heart. It was so good to let them out, especially the anger. In the past, I had always kept anger under cover, and it had simmered away inside me, sometimes spilling out. Then I read in Ephesians 4:26, 'Be angry, but sin not.' I realised that I could be a Christian and still feel angry. The important thing was to avoid harming anyone because of my anger. That was a great revelation to me. I felt able to acknowledge my anger and deal with it, instead of pretending that I wasn't angry. My children have learned to express their feelings too, as they have seen this change take place in me. I have been pleasantly surprised to discover that people prefer the 'real', honest me to the 'artificial' me they knew before; they are now ready to share their own failings and worries with me.

Sue's eating disorders caused our whole family to be shaken up. The nice tidy facade that we had put up was ripped to shreds. We felt exposed and afraid. At one point I complained to God, 'Lord, you promised that you wouldn't test me beyond my endurance, and you are.' But of course he wasn't, because I'm still here to tell the tale. I'm stronger and wiser because of the experience. We have made up for the family life which we missed. We have developed a new openness and ability to communicate. We have spent hours talking about the mistakes that we made, and what we have learned through it all. And we have grown closer together – while retaining our own individuality. Deceitfulness often accompanies eating disorders, and trust between family members can be destroyed. Thankfully, we have been able to re-establish trust, respect and love within the family.

What is even more important, our faith in God has become stronger. We have become less judgmental, and less proud. Suffering tends to strip people of pride, as it gets us right down to the nitty gritty of who we are. Jesus never promised that the Christian life would be easy, but God does promise to give us what we need. I have learned at first hand the truth of God's words, 'My grace is sufficient for you, for my power is made perfect in weakness' (2 Corinthians 12:9). It can be painful to stop and look at ourselves in a closer way, but that was what I really needed to do in order to become more like the person God wanted me to be. I believe that God is pleased with the greater degree of honesty that our lives now show.

My feelings of guilt and the need to 'let go' of Sue, and also my other girls, are two issues which have been ongoing and difficult to deal with. Until very recently, every so often I would become physically ill with flu-like symptoms whenever Sue called to say she was feeling down or having problems of any kind. A sort of sick fear would creep over me and I would go to great lengths to rush to her side and try to help. I felt somehow responsible for her, and I would become both physically and emotionally exhausted. I believe that a lot of my behaviour was motivated from the guilt I still felt deep down inside. Such guilt would crop up every couple of months.

God set me free from this guilt while I was studying on a counselling course. As an assignment, I was recording a personal journal on the computer. Sue was going through some problems at work at this time, and I was feeling ill. After printing out the journal which I had written, I wanted to delete it from the computer, because it was confidential. I thought I had deleted it, but it re-appeared every time I switched the computer back on. I am not very clever with computers, and this happened for several days.

I went off to a ladies prayer meeting, and shared with the women there how low I was feeling. They gathered around me with a genuine love and care, and they prayed for me. When the meeting ended I suddenly realised that I felt much better, and somebody commented that the colour had returned to my cheeks. I went home and looked in the mirror. Sure enough, I had left home with a drawn, ashen face, and now my cheeks were pink and my eyes sparkling. I rushed upstairs to begin my next assignment on the computer. There, to my annoyance, was the piece I had been trying to delete. As I sat looking at it I suddenly knew that God was about to speak to me, and I sat very still. The Lord said, 'I am going to show you where you have been going wrong.' I tried to delete the work as before. As the computer flashed up, 'Do you want to save the changes?' I realised that I had been choosing the option 'No', as I was thinking that I did not want to save the work. Then I realised that I did want to 'save the delete'. I 'saved the delete', and my work was deleted from the computer forever. The Lord said in that still, small voice, 'I have deleted your guilt. I died so that you could be forgiven for the past – now I want you to save the delete. Every time your guilt flashes up on the screen of your mind, reminding you of past mistakes and failings, I want you to remember that I have deleted your sin, forever. I have removed it from you as far as the east is from the west.' Since that time, I have experienced normal guilt feelings from time to time, but the strong hold that guilt had over me has completely gone, and I no longer become ill because of it.

Since Sue's recovery, I have helped to set up a family support section within the organisation Anorexia and Bulimia Care (ABC). This network offers a newsletter for the families of people with eating disorders. I get a lot of pleasure from helping other people who are going through similar problems. While Sue was ill, I couldn't see any point in all the suffering. I said to God, 'Lord, I've told my neighbours I'm a Christian, but you can't hide anorexia – they know we're going through this. Now they are offering to help me, and they feel sorry for me. What must they think? Why are you letting me down, Lord? This is terrible.' I didn't want people to know we had problems. I wanted to keep up the good appearances. Nowadays, our neighbours come to me and say, 'It was marvellous the way you coped through all that – where did you get your strength from?' I can only reply that God gave me strength when I hadn't got any of my own. It wasn't pointless going through it all. Every time I help someone else, I thank God for what he taught me through our experience. I can honestly say, 'Yes, God's hand was in it.' Now we are looking forward to the future, to see what else God is going to do in our lives.

15

Henry – A Husband's Story

As I used to work long hours on a farm, I didn't see many human beings, especially those of the opposite sex. One day, as I was looking through a Christian magazine, I saw an advert about computer dating for Christians. Being a normal country lad, I initially thought the concept was ridiculous. But for some reason I didn't completely dismiss the idea, and I did eventually join the agency. It wasn't very productive for me, as there were not a lot of eligible young ladies in the area where I lived. I rang the agency again and said, 'If you can't find me someone local, forget it – there's no way I can court somebody the other side of the country.' They couldn't find me anyone, so I discontinued my membership, and sort of forgot about it.

At this stage I was still living with my parents. One day I came home for lunch and my mother said, 'There's a letter for you.' I'm the sort who always looks at the handwriting before opening a letter, and I didn't recognise this writing. I opened the letter. Unknown to me, Alice had joined the dating agency just as I had left it, and our paperwork had overlapped. I liked what I was hearing in her letter, although there was no photo in it. She lived forty miles away, which was a bit of a distance, but not impossible.

We wrote to each other a few times, and then we spoke on the phone and agreed to meet. Afterwards, one of my friends asked how the date had been. I told him that I had really liked Alice, as she had a lovely personality, and she was quite a pretty maid (as we say in Devon). But her weight was off-putting.

Although I prefer a well-covered body to a slim one, Alice was more than just well-covered, she was grossly overweight. My friend advised me, 'If you think she's worth having, you can slim her down after you marry her.'

My other friends, and my family members, were less keen on the match. They cautioned me, 'You can't marry her, she doesn't know anything about farming.' It was true, we had completely different backgrounds; I was a farmer, and Alice knew nothing about cows and manure. But we believed that God had brought us together. We had prayed about our relationship, and I could say with confidence, 'I believe the Lord's hand is in it, and it will work.'

Alice and I first met on Saturday the fourth of November. We got engaged the following February, and married in September. We were in our mid-twenties. Alice had lost some weight during our courtship, so that she wasn't so overweight on our wedding day, and I was very happy.

On the first night of our honeymoon, I was lying on our bed while Alice was in the bathroom. I asked the Lord why it was that although Alice said she loved me, she did not seem to want me to touch her, and she could only give 'cold hugs'. I felt that the Lord dropped into my mind a word which I had to share with Alice. To start with, I thought that I must be mistaken. But the word would not go away. The word was 'abuse'. I said, 'What's all this about, Lord? I've never been abused.' I was completely puzzled. I was a farmer, and abuse was something I'd never really thought about or come across.

When Alice came out of the bathroom, I said, 'Look love, I've got this word which keeps coming to me. You'll probably think I'm silly, it seems totally bizarre, but I really feel I have to share it with you. The word is abuse.'

Wow. What an effect that had on Alice! It was as if a bomb had exploded. For the rest of our honeymoon, we discussed this, and Alice cried and cried. She hadn't cried for years, but now she couldn't stop. What I didn't realise at the time was that she wasn't crying for the past and the pain she had experienced, because that was still locked up inside her. She was crying because there she was, on the first few days of our married life, with a husband who adored her, and she thought that I was going to reject her. She thought that once we got home I would want to divorce her, because I wouldn't want to know anybody who had an abusive background. She was horrified because I had said the word which was never meant to be uttered. She felt that her whole life had collapsed all around her. How was she going to cope with this? She felt very mixed up.

People joke about honeymoons – it's the time you should consecrate your marriage. We didn't. We had one flop of a honeymoon. To cope with being abused, Alice had learned to dissociate herself from her body and switch herself off emotionally every time she was touched. It was as if she wasn't there, as if it was someone else who was being touched. That was why she was so unresponsive to me. She had separated out love and touch. She believed that if somebody really loved her, they would love her as a person, and not want her body. She thought that if anyone wanted her body, they could not love her. She found it very hard to accept that I loved her dearly as a person, and also wanted to hold her.

The Lord really worked in my heart and mind during our honeymoon, showing me things about Alice which she didn't even know about herself. He did this for a purpose, to help Alice begin to acknowledge her experiences, so that we would be able to work through the hurts, and go on to build a lovely marriage. Alice started to share her story with me, and it was painful to hear it.

Alice's mother had made it very clear that she only wanted boys, but she had three sons and three daughters. Her boys were everything to her, while her girls were just a nuisance as far as she was concerned. Alice felt that her mother never really gave her the love and encouragement which she needed. Being the second to youngest child, she always felt at the bottom of the pile. The eldest child received a lot of attention, but Alice's mum and dad seemed to have very little energy left for Alice. Her older sister wore nice new clothes, while Alice was given 'hand-me-downs'. She felt very second rate.

When Alice was six or seven years old, one of her brothers, who was much older than her, began to sexually abuse her. He would wait until every member of the family went to sleep, and then come into her bedroom when the lights were out, and abuse her. The family had a pretty big house, but Alice felt that there was nowhere she could go where she would be safe. Not even in her own bedroom, not even when she went to the toilet. This went on for a long time. Alice often used to get sick with one thing or another, and this brother was always the one who was supposed to look after her. He was meant to come home during the school dinner hour and give her some lunch when she was ill. Even in those times she wasn't safe, he would abuse her.

He told Alice that if anyone ever found out their secret, she would be responsible for splitting up her family. It would all be her fault and nobody would love her. She believed him. What a heavy weight that was upon a little child.

On one occasion, her sister walked into the room while Alice was being abused. Alice's heart leaped out of her. She felt very ashamed, and so scared that she could hardly breath. She was terrified that her sister would tell their mother, and that Alice would be responsible for breaking up the family. She thought her world had ended.

However, her brother managed to talk their sister round, and bribe her, giving her some money to buy her silence. He told her that she hadn't seen what she saw and he told her to go away. No more was said.

There were many times when Alice's brother gave her the nod or the wink and she knew he wanted her to make herself available. She tried every means she could think of to get out of it, but she couldn't.

Alice felt, both as a little child and also later as a grown up, that she had to portray that she was happy and in control, and that there weren't any problems in her life. She believed that if she showed the slightest indication that she was unhappy, questions would be asked and if they started delving into her life, she would be bound to tell the truth, and she couldn't do that. Her secret had to remain inside her.

To ensure that she kept quiet, her brother used to give her money when he had a little bit to spare. Alice would go to the local shops and buy sweets. She knew that if she came home with these sweets, she would be asked where she had got the money from, and she wouldn't be able to explain it, so she would gobble them up as quickly as possible, before she got home, so that nobody would question her.

Already, at that young age, eating gave her a little feeling of warmth and comfort. At mealtimes, she would eat as much as she could. One of her sisters was a fussy eater, so Alice would sit next to her, and eat anything which her sister didn't want to finish. She was always compared to this slim sister, and always felt grotesque in comparison.

When visitors came to the house, such as aunts and uncles, or a boyfriend or girlfriend of an older brother or sister, Alice's mind wouldn't be on enjoying the company. Instead, she would be thinking about the extra food which would be available. Her mind was always focused on food. She tolerated school, thinking that when she got home she would get a meal and be able to feel full up again.

By the time Alice was a teenager, filling herself up at mealtimes wasn't enough. She had also started sneaking food out of the kitchen, and eating it secretly. As she was one of six children, there was always plenty of food around, and she could easily take some of it without anyone noticing. After the evening meal, if she felt unhappy, she would creep into the kitchen and take half a dozen biscuits or some cake to eat. She might still feel uncomfortably full from the meal, but she would push herself to eat more anyway. She would pinch whatever food she thought she could get away with. If there were five cakes in a box, she might take one and move the rest around, so it was not obvious that anything had been taken. She always covered her tracks.

Every Saturday evening, Alice and her brothers and sisters, as a treat, were allowed to sit in front of the television and eat sweets. The more they had done to please their parents during the week, the more sweets they were given as a reward. Alice knew how to milk this system. She would be helpful all week, so that she could receive a lot of sweets on the Saturday evening and satisfy her craving to eat. Alice's mother used to like having her feet rubbed. Nobody else would do this, but Alice would sit on the floor and rub her feet for half an hour, so that she would receive more sweets.

Her mother used to make comments which knocked Alice down, over and over again. She discovered that it was easiest just to do everything her mother wanted, whatever it cost her. She didn't want to get her mother annoyed, she wanted to keep her happy, so that Alice could have a peaceful life.

As a young adult, Alice felt completely worthless and helpless. Her hopelessness was demonstrated in her eating behaviour, which was out of control. Food was like a warm coat, and she was wrapping herself up in this coat, to hide and protect herself. When she was fifteen she left school and started earning money in a factory. That opened up new opportunities to buy food. She paid for her keep, but she could do whatever she wanted to with the rest of her money. Suddenly, she was able to go to the next town and buy pasties, hamburgers or sweets. She would eat them all while she was out, and then go home, and nobody would know about it. She made sure that she had some money left, so that her parents did not ask what she was spending all her money on, because that had to remain a secret.

A year later, Alice decided to go to college. Finances were

tight, but she was still able to eat small mountains of food. Later on, she ate bigger mountains. She felt unable to stop herself and her weight rose steadily, her clothes size going up from 12 to 20. Whenever she had a boyfriend she would lose weight, back down to a size 16, by drastically cutting down on what she was eating. She thought that having a partner would solve her problems. But the relationship would end, because Alice was emotionally confused. The pounds would pile on again, until someone else took her out. She had a wardrobe of clothes of each size.

Alice would do anything to please anyone, whatever it cost her, in the hope of being loved. She found it very difficult to form close relationships with people, especially with men. She thought they were all the same, and just wanted her for sex. Nothing else. Alice couldn't conceive of the idea that they wanted to get to know her in any more meaningful, lasting way. Time and time again she fell into the trap of meeting a man, quickly finding herself in bed with him, and immediately afterwards switching off and rejecting him. She did not want to do what she was doing, and in fact she found it very frightening. She was looking for the love which she so desperately needed, but in the wrong avenue. She had been used by men, and she was using men, because she didn't know what a proper relationship was. It was one disaster after another.

When she was seventeen, her father died quite suddenly. This had a profound effect on her. There was her dad, aged forty-nine, finally managing to get all his children off his hands, and then he was just taken. Her mother blamed God, and couldn't understand, if God was a God of justice and love, why he had taken her husband. It didn't make any sense to Alice either. At that time she had a very good school friend who had become a born-again Christian, and they would talk together about their lives. Her friend encouraged Alice to go to church, but Alice was a bit sceptical, wondering what Christianity was all about.

Eventually she did go into an Anglican church. Her preset idea was that churches were all stuffy, with old-fashioned hymns from the ark. What she saw in front of her was completely different. It was interesting and bright and cheerful. There were lots of young people, and there was a praise and worship group with musicians and singers. It was quite exciting. She started going along week after week, and before she knew it she was really enjoying it. What was amazing was that she was actually listening to the sermons. As the weeks went by, the word 'love' kept coming to her. She heard that God really loved her, God cared and God wanted her. She realised that God was giving her the love which she felt was missing in her life. He was saying that she was so special that even if she had been the only person on earth, he would still have sent Jesus to die for her. Not long after making this awesome discovery, Alice committed her life to Jesus.

Alice felt that her whole life had been a pretence, an act. People had just seen what she wanted to show them. They had no idea what was really going on inside her. She was still looking for someone who could really know her and love her, but she felt that she had reached the end of her ability to choose a partner.

Then she noticed a little advert in a paper, for a Christian dating agency. She ignored it, thinking 'This is daft', but she kept coming across it, again and again. So she prayed about whether or not she should respond. She felt that it was right for her to contact the agency, and so she did. She prayed, 'Lord, as far as I'm concerned, men are all the same. If you want me to have a husband, you sort it out.'

Soon afterwards, she was sent my details. Ten months later, we were married. Everything seemed great. Then God gave me the word 'abuse', and everything changed. Not only did I have to deal with an abused and hurting wife, I had to deal with how I felt about it. As Alice's story came out, I struggled with the fact that I had assumed that she was a virgin, but she wasn't. I can't pretend that didn't matter to me, because it did. I was expecting a new parcel, not used paper, for the want of a better expression. It took time to work through our emotions, but the bottom line was that I loved her. It must be difficult for someone who is not a Christian to work through this sort of situation. We felt that it was the Lord who helped us through. I thought about how Jesus had been abused — in a different sort of way — before he had been hung on the cross. He received us for what we were, and I was willing to receive Alice for who she was. As far as I'm concerned, marriage is a commitment for life. There's no condition in the Bible that says, 'If your wife has been sexually abused you can divorce her.' If you love somebody, you freely give yourself to that person, and I was determined to continue loving Alice, whatever we might have to go through.

Over the years Alice had buried many painful memories in the back of her mind, thinking that she must never let anyone know the truth about her. She believed that if anyone knew, they would think that she was dirty and trash, and she would be rejected all over again. She couldn't face that, and so she decided it would be a secret until the day she died, and she tried to forget. Little did she know that God had other plans! In the early years of our marriage, very gently, God allowed the memories to come back to her. The Lord even dropped names into my mind, to help the process along. I would be milking a cow, and a name would come into my mind and stick there. I would go back to Alice and say, 'Does the name so-and-so mean anything to you?' She didn't have to answer me. I would see from her eyes that it did. I would say, 'Right, we need to sit down and talk this one through.'

I didn't know much about counselling or anything like that. But I had been a Christian since I was seventeen, and sometimes I was able to see things from a Christian perspective when Alice couldn't, as she had only been a Christian for a few years. I offered Alice all the support I could. We didn't feel that we could talk about the situation with anyone else, not even with people at our church. Sexual abuse was more of a taboo subject then than it is now. For eighteen months we prayed about the situation, without mentioning it to anyone else. We both loved Jesus and knew that somehow he wanted to help us, but we didn't have a clue about what we should do.

All this time, as Alice was remembering more and more about her childhood, she was eating large quantities of food in an attempt to help her cope with her feelings. It took a long time for her to acknowledge to me that she had eating problems. I became aware quite early on that something was not right. Being a farmer, doing physically demanding work all day, I could eat quite a bit. I would come home in the evening, and Alice would dish up dinner. She would hand me a large plateful of food – perhaps five pieces of meat, five potatoes and gravy. She would have an identical portion herself. Sometimes I had to say in the middle of the meal, 'I'm sorry love, I can't get through all this.' Then she would finish hers, and polish off mine as well. She never felt that this was unusual, but I did. In my family the men who did the active work always ate large portions, but the women who stayed at home ate far more modest amounts. If I mentioned this, Alice would become upset, thinking that I had no right to comment on what she was eating – she was grown up and married, and had the right to eat as much as I did if she wanted to. I didn't object to her eating as much as me, but it did puzzle me.

Alice had been taught to eat everything which was on her plate. She would put every ounce of energy into clearing her plate, as she couldn't justify leaving anything. If we went out for a meal and the serving dishes were left on the table, she felt compelled to empty the dishes. Every morsel of food on the table had to be consumed.

Sometimes I would go to our cupboard and think, 'There were four buns left – where have they got to?' I'm quite partial to chocolate, and from time to time Alice bought a bar for me.

I would eat half of it, and put the rest in the fridge for the next day. The next day I would ask Alice, 'Where's the chocolate gone? Have the kids eaten it?' She could have lied, but she would always be honest and reply, 'No, I ate it'. When it became a regular pattern, I would ask her, puzzled, 'Couldn't you have waited until tonight and we could have shared it?'

There were times when Alice's eating did not appear to be too much of a problem, but at other times she binged on vast amounts of food. She would say 'OK, I'll have one biscuit,' and the one would become ten, then twenty, and she would eat until there was nothing left. She felt dreadful about herself, and we couldn't understand why she behaved in this way. She knew that I loved her; she had good friends around her; she had a good church life; we had lovely children, but she would lose control. We didn't realise that her eating problem was related to everything which she had been through in the past.

I tried various tactics to help her eat less. I went through a stage when I felt I had to bully her, and watch what she was eating. That didn't help. She would notice my look, and ask defensively, 'What are you looking at me for?' and eat even more. Then I tried ignoring her eating patterns. She seemed to like that, but she tended to eat even more. She would eat and eat and eat all day, topping herself up whenever she could, until she went to bed. The next morning she would start the day thinking, 'I'm going to eat properly,' but by afternoon she would binge again.

Alice put on so much weight that even her largest clothes no longer fitted her. When she got upset about this, I would tell her that it didn't matter whether her clothes said size 16 or size 22 – she was still Alice, the one I loved. I would love her the same whether she weighed twenty-two stone or five stone. I had long since lost the desire to 'slim her down'. I learned to tell her that I loved her, no matter what she ate, or what she weighed. I used to say over and over again, 'You're beautiful, you're important and I love you,' until she could believe this. We have all fallen short of God's glory, but he still loves us. And I loved Alice, despite her weaknesses.

I found it difficult to understand her eating problem, though, and I would ask her, 'Why?' We would sit down and talk it through, and cry together. I often tried to put myself in her situation. If I had been abused, I would want somebody to love me and look after me and come alongside me, and help me work it through; so I tried to provide that support for Alice. It wasn't easy. There were times when I just wanted to run away, but if you run, the problem's still there. God helped us to face the problem, instead of running from it.

One day when Alice was in the kitchen, crying to God for help, she felt that she should get a pen and paper. This was very unusual for her, as she tended to avoid writing. She had found it difficult to concentrate when she was at school, because of everything that was going on at home, and so she had experienced difficulty learning, and had never become confident about writing. Nevertheless, on this occasion she felt that God wanted her to write something. He gave her a poem. Words which she hadn't been able to say, now looked up at her from the page. After this there were a number of occasions when God gave her words which expressed how she was feeling, and she wrote them down. This helped her to acknowledge the feelings which she had locked away inside her. God helped her to recognise her feelings, and she felt that he would have to help her deal with them, as she had no idea what she should do with them.

The worst time for Alice took place about four years ago. By this time we had three children. Alice had been managing to eat in a relatively normal manner, but suddenly she spun out of control again. She started to eat more than ever. She felt so disgusting, and so afraid of gaining even more weight, that she began to make herself sick after eating. She felt desperate, but she was able to be honest with me about this problem. We prayed together for a long time, and then Alice found the courage to tell a friend about her eating problem, and about the sexual abuse as well. This friend spoke with another friend, who provided the phone number of a Christian who counselled people with eating difficulties. God had allowed the memories to surface, so that Alice would be willing to accept help, and so the root of the problem could be dealt with. Now God had provided someone to help. It felt like the light at the end of the tunnel.

When Alice first saw the counsellor, we were very naive. We thought that with one or two counselling sessions, Alice could deal with all her problems and put them behind her. In reality, Alice received many, many sessions of counselling. Sometimes I attended the appointments with her. Through the counselling, we realised that Alice had used food like a tranquillizer, to help her avoid thinking about her pain. She had reached out to food to comfort her. She was saying, 'Help! I need help! I need love! I need to get through this situation that I'm facing,' but she was asking food to help her.

For many years, Alice had felt unable to cry. She thought that if she shed tears, someone would ask her what was wrong with her, and she wouldn't be able to cope with that. Through receiving counselling, she learned to express her emotions. If she shouted because she was upset, I would give her a cuddle, then she might burst into tears, which might be just what she needed at that time. Then we would talk about it.

It was very painful to go back and deal with all the trauma and despair, but Alice knew that Jesus would take her step by step through the healing process. He did. He showed her his love and his care. She was able to talk about the pain which she had experienced, and to pray about it, and receive God's grace. She started to feel free from the burdens which she had carried.

Although Alice knew that God was a loving God, she felt a lot of anger towards him. She knew that God sees everything, and so he saw all the abuse. She used to think, 'God, you made me, you're the one who put the breath in my body, and yet you allowed the abuse to happen – why? Why did you put me with those parents, that family? Why did you allow these people to do that to me?' With her counsellor, she allowed the anger from deep within her to come out. Then she realised that God knew her even before she was born. He knew from the beginning *everything* that was going to happen to her. He did not cause the pain – it was caused by the sin of others. When she suffered, he felt the pain even more than she did. He had given her the strength to carry on. God could have changed the situation, but he allowed her to go through the pain, and he brought good out of it. Through experiencing the pain, she has become the person that she is now. It was through the lack of love that she came to know Jesus. What would she have achieved if her childhood had been happy but she had not come to know God? Alice knows that God cares for her so much that he has not left her in pain. He has taken her on to where she is today, and he is going to remain with her for eternity. Alice was delighted when she was able to let go of the anger which she felt towards God.

Both Alice and I also had to deal with the extreme anger which we felt towards key people whose actions seemed to have messed up her whole life. I wanted to throttle them, especially the brother who had abused her, because I knew that her life would have been completely different if that had never happened. I felt very angry with Alice's mother as well, for not taking care of Alice as a mother should. Children really need, from day one, to receiving nurturing love so that they can feel secure in their environment and develop and grow to be the adults God wants them to be. Alice never really received that input. She believed that if she had, then she would have been able to tell her mother what was happening when the abuse started, and it could have been stopped before it got out of hand. Nothing was shared in their family. Sex, in particular, was considered a dirty word which couldn't be mentioned. Alice's mother even considered menstruation to be degrading. When

Alice had her first period, she had to deal with it on her own and in secret, as her mother didn't want to know about it. As a result, Alice felt unclean and disgusted. To mention abuse was unthinkable.

The counselling sessions helped us to realise that we will never know what was going on in the minds of the people who had wronged Alice, including her mother. Something in their lives must have happened to lead them to act in the way in which they did. We spoke with God about our feelings of anger. We came to realise that we had to choose to forgive, if we were going to be completely set free to be the people God wanted us to be. We knew from Scripture that God wanted us to forgive, so that he could in turn forgive us and give us all that he wanted in our lives, without bitterness being in the way. God does not like all the things we do, but he really loves us all, and he forgives us. We wanted to learn to forgive as well. We came to understand that forgiveness is a choice rather than a feeling. We asked God to help us forgive, and to free us from our anger and bitterness; it took time, but with his help, we came to the point where we could honestly say that although we didn't like the situation, and Alice had been badly wronged, we did truly forgive those involved. God has given us compassion for them, and now we are even able to welcome Alice's brother into our home. If Alice hears his name or thinks about him, she no longer feels angry or afraid. Alice also feels a lot of love towards her mother, and regularly prays for her, phones her and tries to help her, hoping that God's love will shine through our lives, and touch her life. Forgiving people for big things has been a great training ground, so that we are now also able to forgive people for the little things that crop up.

Even as an adult, Alice had been afraid that if her secret came out she would break up the family. That had a great hold on her. As she forgave, she found that the people involved no longer had any hold over her. Gradually, she came to realise that the situation was in God's hands. He helped her to overcome her fear not only in this area, but also in many other areas. She used to even be afraid of going to the supermarket without me. I would drive her there, go in with her, help her fill the trolley, pay and take her out to the car. She depended on me. Then there came a time when she had to do this all on her own. She didn't want to, she felt scared; she felt that she had been out of society when she was at home all the time bringing up our children and she had lost her confidence, and found it difficult to become integrated into society again. We talked about this and prayed, and Alice felt released from the fear. Now she is able to go anywhere on her own, without being crippled by fear. She has come to believe that whatever happens in the future, God will be with her in it.

In the last few years, Alice has been able to stand up in church and give testimony to the fact that God has enabled her to overcome difficulties associated with being sexually abused. That has been a tremendous release for her, because up until this point she was too afraid to talk about the abuse, as she thought people would reject her. Because of the healing which God has brought her, she has been able to acknowledge her background, and this has brought an indescribable freedom.

At first Alice found it hard to discipline our three children, because she feared that they would hate her if she did. She had to learn that it is right to discipline children, lovingly, because that is what God wants us to do. Children need to know that we love them so much that we are prepared to discipline them, in their best interests, to teach them to distinguish right from wrong. Alice and I are now able to agree on a consistent, loving but firm way in which to bring up our children and they are happy little people!

For years, Alice decided every few months to try going on a diet. She would lose a little bit of weight, but as soon as anybody commented on her weight loss, she would feel as if she had been cut with a knife, and she would be unable to cope with the fact that people had noticed her. She would then flip the other way and regain the weight which she had lost, and more. She felt secure with the extra pounds covering her, and yet at the same time she desperately wanted to lose weight. As she continued to receive counselling, her weight became less important to her. She started to realise how God saw her – that he really values her, and that she is special in his eyes. Her priorities changed, and she began to feel better about herself. She became able to accept herself, regardless of her size. Now, size and weight are pretty irrelevant to Alice. She is learning to just be, for today. She is not worried about tomorrow, or about the past, or about comments from other people. She feels free, and we are learning to enjoy life to the full. In the past she allowed rubbish to get into her life, and she kept love and good things out. She has turned that around, so that now she rejects all the garbage, and allows God's love, and love from other people, to penetrate deep within her. She knows that she has been forgiven for all the wrong relationships she was involved in. God has shown her the person he wants her to be – this is not the person she thought she should be to please everybody else. She doesn't have to hide and pretend any more, as she can be open and honest. She can be Alice.

Alice doesn't binge any more, and she dishes up much smaller portions for herself. She is able to leave food on her plate if she has had enough. Her weight has not gone up for quite a long time, and she has even lost some weight without really trying. She now weighs about fourteen stone. That might sound heavy, but she was seventeen stone, so for her it is very good. She feels much better. The doctor checks her weight and her blood pressure for health reasons. Alice would still like to be a bit lighter, but she believes this will be in God's time, and she knows he'll help her. For the time being, she has taken the pressure off herself and has learned to be patient with herself. She believes that if people don't accept her for who she is, that's their problem. She can accept the weight she is. It's the surgery which God is doing *inside* her which matters most at the moment.

God doesn't just want to heal us from the past, he wants to deal with today's issues too. Now, if Alice heads towards the fridge when she doesn't need something to eat, she is able to catch herself, and to ask, 'Why am I doing this?' It very rarely happens now, but if it does, she will immediately tell me about the problem. This is a great sign of progress, as it used to take her weeks before she felt able to tell me about it. Often the Lord reveals what the difficulty is, and we pray about the situation, talk it through and deal with it. It might simply be that I've said something which has caused Alice to feel angry, in which case we can quickly sort it out and make up. If Alice needs to have time on her own to deal with what we have discussed, I ensure that she can get that space. If we come across anything which we feel we need more support with, Alice goes back to see the counsellor for a one-off session. She no longer needs to use food to meet her emotional needs.

God brought us together, and I care a great deal for Alice. Sometimes I haven't known how to help her, but I try to always be there for her, and to offer a shoulder to cry on when she needs it. However, I have discovered that I don't always have to be the strong one in the relationship, as Alice can support me too. In the past, if I felt a bit down, Alice would panic and feel unable to cope. She now realises that it's OK for me to feel low sometimes. She has learned that although we are 'one flesh' as man and wife, she does not need to feel low if I do. We support each other.

Every individual is unique, and every situation is slightly different, so there is no one way to overcome eating problems. God knows where each of us is hurting. He knows our inner-most depths, even if we haven't faced them ourselves yet. If we trust him, he will gently take us step by step on our journey towards wholeness. He will show us where to go, when we are ready to face the next step. Alice and I believe that we can help other couples, because of what we have been through. We don't want other people to feel inferior because they have not yet reached the place of healing which we have reached. It has taken us years, and we haven't been strong all the time. There are times when I've wanted to run away, or scream, or cry. Without God's help we would never have got here. Everyone goes at a different speed, but God can help each one. The greater the mountain, the greater the victory.

My message to other people who are married to someone who has an eating disorder is that however difficult it is, you should try to be open, be truthful and keep telling them that you love them. People who feel loved, accepted and secure can cope with life a lot better, whatever hurdles they may have to cross. Most of all, be patient, stick with it, and keep reaching out to the Lord, because he hears your cries. If necessary, find someone you can share your own feelings with. We have learned that we can deal with whatever is chucked at us, because God will never put us through more than we can cope with.

We praise God for all that he has done in our lives. He has given us many Scripture verses which have been a tremendous encouragement to us, and have helped us to get to where we are today. We are confident that God will complete the good work which he has begun in us.

Afterword:
Some Final Words from Debbie

Life never stands still. During the few months between finishing the draft for this book and waiting for its publication, my life has changed quite dramatically.

I spent Christmas 1999 with my mum and my brother. My mum helped to proofread this book during that time, and appeared pleased that I had written it. We had a happy holiday together, and enjoyed playing some silly games, such as racing round her flat holding coins between our toes!

Less than a month later, my mum suddenly became very ill. She went into hospital in February, and seven weeks later she died. She had been suffering from a fast-growing form of cancer which was resistant to chemotherapy.

For the last two weeks of her life I stayed with her in the hospital – as did my brother, my sister and my father. On a day when she was unconscious, I held her hand and said to her that sometimes when I felt unwell, I liked to think about heaven – the place where there is no more suffering, no tears, no separation or death or loneliness or depression, but rather a place of joy, being in the presence of God. To my surprise, my mother started to nod her head up and down as I said this, although it had been assumed that she was unconscious and unable to move. I knew that she was ready to meet her God.

During her last five nights alive, my brother and sister and I sat through the night with her, so that she was not left alone. It was obvious to everyone who saw us that, whatever had happened in the past, we were now a close and loving family. Mum died peacefully in her sleep, but not before I had the chance to once again tell her how much I loved her, and to thank her for all she had done for me. And also to tell her my secret about a planned future engagement. But that's another story.

Appendix

Further Help and Information

Useful Addresses, Websites and Books

People with eating difficulties can ask their GP to refer them to somebody who can help them, such as a clinical psychologist or a psychiatrist. There is no charge for National Health Service referrals.

Some people prefer to make their own arrangements to see a counsellor privately, paying for this themselves. EDA (address below) can give information about counsellors with a special interest in eating disorders, in each region of the UK. The Christian Counsellors Directory is useful for finding a Christian counsellor; copies can be obtained from Grace Ministries, phone/fax 01903 521462. If this is not successful, the Association of Christian Counsellors (address below) may be able to help.

ADDRESSES

Anorexia and Bulimia Care (ABC)
ABC is a Christian charity which offers support to anyone with an eating disorder, and to their carers, families and friends. Resources available from ABC include a 'starter pack' for people who are thinking about moving forward in their recovery; a 'church pack' (resources for churches supporting people with eating disorders); quarterly newsletters for people with eating

disorders and for carers; details about support groups; 'FaithLift' days throughout the UK (which include the use of art and music, and small group discussions, with other people affected by eating disorders), and prayer support. ABC also offers leaflets on relevant topics. (For example, the leaflet 'The Truth Can Set You Free' describes how to replace negative thoughts with biblical truths.) Leaflets, books and cassettes, including a relaxation tape, can be purchased or borrowed from ABC. ABC is also involved with preventative work in schools.

ABC offers a 'befrienders scheme', through which people with eating problems are linked up with a befriender (usually someone who has recovered from an eating disorder). Similarly, carers can be linked up with people who are able to support them. ABC would be very happy to hear from people who might be interested in becoming befrienders, as well as those who would like to receive support.

Contact: ABC, PO Box 30, Ormskirk, Lancs, L39 5JR. Tel: 01695 422479. E-mail: doreen.abc@virgin.net. Website: http://www.AnorexiaBulimiaCare.co.uk

Association of Christian Counsellors (ACC)
Although ACC is not primarily a referral service, they will do their best to help people find a counsellor. They can usually put you in touch with a representative who can provide information about trained, accredited Christian counsellors in your area.

Contact: ACC, 173a Wokingham Road, Reading, Berkshire, RG6 ILU. Tel: 0118 966 2207.

British Association of Counselling (BAC)
BAC has a list of counsellors who deal with eating disorders, including specialists in children's eating disorders.

Contact: BAC, 1 Regents Place, Rugby, CV21 1PJ. Tel: 01788 578328.

Burrswood

Burrswood is a Christian centre for healthcare and ministry. Based in Kent, Burrswood offers professional in-patient and out-patient support in a caring atmosphere, for people with a range of medical or emotional difficulties. Although unable to offer long-term treatment for people with eating disorders, Burrswood can offer counselling over a short period (for example, a three-week stay).

Contact: Burrswood, Groombridge, Tunbridge Wells, Kent, TN3 9PY. Tel: 01892 863637. Fax: 01892 862597. E-mail: enquiries@burrswood.org.uk. Website: http://www.burrswood.org.uk

CARE

CARE is a Christian organisation committed to demonstrating Christ's compassion, in many different ways. CARE maintains a database of caring agencies throughout the UK. CARE also operates a programme through which Christians open up their homes for short periods to people who are experiencing difficulties, or to carers who would like a break for a few days.

Contact: CARE, 53 Romney Street, London, SW1P 3RF. Tel: 0171 233 0455. Fax: 0171 233 0983. E-mail: mail@care.org.uk. Website: http://www.care.org.uk

Christian Survivors of Sexual Abuse (CSSA)

CSSA is a Christian organisation dedicated to helping those who have been sexually abused. CSSA send out a newsletter, and details about support groups and seminars.

Contact: BM CSSA, London, WC1 3XX.

Depression Alliance

This organisation provides information and support to all who suffer from clinical depression and their carers. They provide a quarterly newsletter, a network of self-help groups, a pen-friend scheme and a written advisory service.

Contact: 35 Westminster Bridge Road, London, SE1 7JB. Tel: 0171 721 7411.

Eating Disorders Association (EDA)

EDA is a national organisation which offers help to people suffering from eating disorders and those who care about them. Unlike ABC, EDA is not a Christian organisation. EDA offers a newsletter; lists of relevant books and leaflets; a network of support groups, and information about treatment over the telephone for people with bulimia. EDA can also provide information about counsellors and other professionals in each region of the UK who have a special interest in eating disorders, as well as specialist treatment centres. EDA provides information about volunteers throughout the UK who are willing to provide help or information over the phone or by letter. Free training is offered to people who would like to become volunteers for EDA.

Contact: First floor, Wensum House, 103 Prince of Wales Road, Norwich, Norfolk, NR1 1DW. Helpline: 01603 621414 (9 am–6.30 pm Mon–Fri). Youth helpline (18 years and under): 01603 765050 (4–6 pm Mon–Fri). E-mail: info@edauk.com Website: http://www.edauk.com

Home Study Course

Christine Lewis is a Christian counsellor who also has a degree in nutrition. She has produced a home study course for individuals who have difficulties with compulsive eating or bulimia. The course can be worked through alone, but can be even more beneficial if it is used with the help of a caring friend, support group or counsellor. The course includes a 'free to choose' manual, which leads step by step through the processes of change and recovery. The manual discusses lifestyle, eating habits and the way that emotions and thoughts are involved. A workbook and a nutrition resource book are also included. The materials are written from a Christian perspective. The course costs £20, including postage and packaging (cheques payable to Christine Lewis), and can be ordered from the address below.

A resource list describing other materials available from Christine Lewis can be obtained by sending a stamped addressed envelope (specifying request for resource list) to: Christine Lewis, Estoril, Onslow Road, Sunningdale, Berkshire, SL5 OHW. 9PY. Website: http:// www.virginiawater.co.uk/eatingdisorders

Kainos Trust

Kainos Trust is a Christian Charitable Trust established by Helena Wilkinson, who has herself recovered from anorexia nervosa. The focus of Kainos is prayer, teaching and personal support. Kainos offers residential weeks and weekends for people who are trying to recover from eating disorders. These include times of interactive teaching covering nutritional, emotional and spiritual issues.

Contact: The Lower George House, Newnham-on-Severn, Gloucestershire, GL14 1BS. Tel and Fax (administration only): 01594 516284.

Overeaters Anonymous (OA)

OA grew out of the 'Alcoholics Anonymous' movement, and uses the same process of Twelve Steps to recovery. OA support groups are held throughout the UK.

Contact: OA, PO Box 19, Stretford, Manchester, M32 9EB. Tel: 01426 984674.

Remuda Ranch

Remuda Ranch is a large Christian treatment centre for people with eating disorders, in Arizona, USA. People from all over the world receive treatment here.

Contact: Remuda Ranch, 10000 N. 31st Avenue, Suite D-

400, Phoenix, Arizona 85051, USA. Tel: (602) 861-0600. Fax: (602) 861-6981. E-mail: remuda@goodnet.com Website: www.remuda-ranch.com

Riverdale Grange

Riverdale Grange in Sheffield offers residential or non-residential therapy for people with anorexia or bulimia. Both private patients and those funded by a health authority are welcome.

Contact: Riverdale Grange, 93 Riverdale Road, Ranmoor, Sheffield. S10 3FE. Tel: 0114 230 2140.

Self-harm helpline

This national helpline is run by the Bristol crisis service for women. Women who engage in self-injury are especially welcome to phone. The helpline is available on Fridays and Saturdays from 9 pm–12.30 am. Tel: 01272 251119.

Websites

At the time of writing, there are more than 18,000 pages on the World Wide Web devoted to eating disorders. Two good websites to start with are:

http://www.noah.cuny.edu/wellconn/eatdisorders.html (available in Spanish and English) and

http://www.mirror-mirror.org/

See also the ABC and EDA websites, listed above.

RECOMMENDED BOOKS

(Books written from a Christian perspective are marked *.)

*Anderson, N.T., *The Bondage Breaker* (London: Monarch, 1990); *Victory Over the Darkness* (London: Monarch, 1990).

*Ashton, M., *A Mind at Ease* (Alresford: Overcomer Publications, 1987).

*Backus, B. and Chapian, M., *Telling Yourself the Truth* (Bethany House, 1980).

Bryant-Waugh, R.. and Lask, B., *Eating Disorders – A Parents' Guide* (Drayton, Middlesex: Penguin, 1999).

Cooper, P.J., *Bulimia Nervosa: A Guide to Recovery* (Robinson Publishing, 1993). Includes a self-help manual.

Crisp, A. et al., *Anorexia Nervosa and the Wish to Change* (Psychology Press, 1996). Includes self-help exercises.

Dickson, A.A., *Woman in Your Own Right* (London: Quartet Books, 1982). On assertiveness.

Fairburn, C., *Overcoming Binge Eating* (Guilford Press, 1995). Includes a self-help manual.

*Friends in Recovery, *The Twelve Steps for Christians* (Recovery Publications Inc, 1988).

Hirshmann, J. and Munter, C., *Overcoming Overeating* (Trudo: Cedar Books, 1994).

*Lovell, D., *Hungry for Love* (Leicester: IVP, 1994). Out of print, but can be requested from local libraries, or borrowed from the library of Anorexia and Bulimia Care.

Roth, G., *Breaking Free from Compulsive Eating* (London: Signet, 1986).

Rowe, D., *Depression and the Way out of Your Prison* (London: Routledge, 1973).

Schmidt, U. and Treasure, J., *Getting Better Bit(e) by Bit(e)* (Lawrence Erlbaum Associates, 1993). A self-help manual for people with bulimia nervosa or binge-eating disorders.

*Urquhart, C., *My Dear Child* (London: Hodder & Stoughton, 1990).

*Wilkinson, H., *Beyond Chaotic Eating* (London: Marshall Pickering, 1993).

*Wilkinson, H., *Puppet on a String* (London: Hodder & Stoughton, 1984).